A Japanese Miscellany

Ōyama no O-Kon San wa . . .

see page 170

LAFCADIO HEARN

A Japanese Miscellany

STRANGE STORIES ~ FOLKLORE GLEANINGS ~ STUDIES HERE & THERE

RUTLAND   VERMONT
CHARLES E. TUTTLE COMPANY
TOKYO   JAPAN

Published by the Charles E. Tuttle Company of
Rutland, Vermont & Tokyo, Japan, with editorial
offices at 27, 1-chome, Morimoto-cho, Azabu, Minato-
ku, Tokyo. Reproduced photographically from the first
American edition, published by Little, Brown, and
Company, Boston, 1901.

First printing, April 1954
Second printing, August 1954

Manufactured in Japan by
Shinyodo Printing Co., Tokyo

Contents

STRANGE STORIES

Of a Promise Kept[1]

❧

"I SHALL return in the early autumn," said Akana Soyëmon several hundred years ago, — when bidding good-bye to his brother by adoption, young Hasébé Samon. The time was spring; and the place was the village of Kato in the province of Harima. Akana was an Izumo samurai; and he wanted to visit his birthplace.

Hasébé said : —

"Your Izumo, — the Country of the Eight-Cloud Rising,[2] — is very distant. Perhaps it will therefore be difficult for you to promise to return here upon any particular day. But, if we were to know the exact day, we should feel happier. We could then prepare a feast of welcome;

---

[1] Related in the *Ugétsu Monogatari*.

[2] One of the old poetical names for the Province of Izumo, or Unshū.

and we could watch at the gateway for your coming."

"Why, as for that," responded Akana, "I have been so much accustomed to travel that I can usually tell beforehand how long it will take me to reach a place; and I can safely promise you to be here upon a particular day. Suppose we say the day of the festival Chōyō?"

"That is the ninth day of the ninth month," said Hasébé; — "then the chrysanthemums will be in bloom, and we can go together to look at them. How pleasant! . . . So you promise to come back on the ninth day of the ninth month?"

"On the ninth day of the ninth month," repeated Akana, smiling farewell. Then he strode away from the village of Kato in the province of Harima; — and Hasébé Samon and the mother of Hasébé looked after him with tears in their eyes.

"Neither the Sun nor the Moon," says an old Japanese proverb, "ever halt upon their journey." Swiftly the months went by; and the autumn came, — the season of chrysanthemums. And early upon the morning of the ninth day of

the ninth month Hasébé prepared to welcome his
adopted brother. He made ready a feast of good
things, bought wine, decorated the guest-room,
and filled the vases of the alcove with chrysanthemums of two colors. Then his mother,
watching him, said : — " The province of Izumo,
my son, is more than one hundred *ri*[1] from this
place ; and the journey thence over the mountains is difficult and weary ; and you cannot be
sure that Akana will be able to come to-day.
Would it not be better, before you take all this
trouble, to wait for his coming ? " " Nay,
mother ! " Hasébé made answer — " Akana
promised to be here to-day : he could not break
a promise ! And if he were to see us beginning
to make preparation after his arrival, he would
know that we had doubted his word ; and we
should be put to shame."

The day was beautiful, the sky without a
cloud, and the air so pure that the world seemed
to be a thousand miles wider than usual. In the
morning many travellers passed through the
village — some of them samurai ; and Hasébé,
watching each as he came, more than once im-

---

[1] A *ri* is about equal to two and a half English miles.

agined that he saw Akana approaching. But the temple-bells sounded the hour of midday; and Akana did not appear. Through the afternoon also Hasébé watched and waited in vain. The sun set; and still there was no sign of Akana. Nevertheless Hasébé remained at the gate, gazing down the road. Later his mother went to him, and said: — " The mind of a man, my son, — as our proverb declares — may change as quickly as the sky of autumn. But your chrysan-themum-flowers will still be fresh to-morrow. Better now to sleep; and in the morning you can watch again for Akana, if you wish." " Rest well, mother," returned Hasébé; — " but I still believe that he will come." Then the mother went to her own room; and Hasébé lingered at the gate.

The night was pure as the day had been: all the sky throbbed with stars; and the white River of Heaven shimmered with unusual splendor. The village slept; — the silence was broken only by the noise of a little brook, and by the far-away barking of peasants' dogs. Hasébé still waited, — waited until he saw the thin moon sink behind the neighboring hills. Then at last he began to doubt and to fear. Just as he was about to re-enter the house, he perceived in the distance a tall man approaching, — very lightly and quickly; and in the next moment he recognized Akana.

"Oh!" cried Hasébé, springing to meet him — "I have been waiting for you from the morning until now! . . . So you really did keep your promise after all. . . . But you must be tired, poor brother! — come in; — everything is ready for you." He guided Akana to the place of honor in the guest-room, and hastened to trim the lights, which were burning low. "Mother," continued Hasébé, "felt a little tired this evening, and she has already gone to bed; but I shall awaken her presently." Akana shook his head, and made a little gesture of disapproval. "As you will, brother," said Hasébé; and he set warm food and wine before the traveller. Akana did not touch the food or the wine, but remained motionless and silent for a short time. Then, speaking in a whisper, — as if fearful of awakening the mother, he said : —

"Now I must tell you how it happened that I came thus late. When I returned to Izumo I found that the people had almost forgotten the kindness of our former ruler, the good Lord Enya, and were seeking the favor of the usurper

Tsunéhisa, who had possessed himself of the Tonda Castle. But I had to visit my cousin, Akana Tanji, though he had accepted service under Tsunéhisa, and was living, as a retainer, within the castle grounds. He persuaded me to present myself before Tsunéhisa: I yielded chiefly in order to observe the character of the new ruler, whose face I had never seen. He is a skilled soldier, and of great courage; but he is cunning and cruel. I found it necessary to let him know that I could never enter into his service. After I left his presence he ordered my cousin to detain me — to keep me confined within the house. I protested that I had promised to return to Harima upon the ninth day of the ninth month; but I was refused permission to go. I then hoped to escape from the castle at night; but I was constantly watched; and until to-day I could find no way to fulfil my promise. . . ."

"Until to-day!" exclaimed Hasébé in bewilderment; — "the castle is more than a hundred *ri* from here!"

"Yes," returned Akana; "and no living man can travel on foot a hundred *ri* in one day. But I felt that, if I did not keep my promise, you could not think well of me; and I remembered the ancient proverb, *Tama yoku ichi nichi ni sen ri wo yuku* [" The soul of a man can journey a thousand *ri* in a day "]. Fortunately I had been allowed to keep my sword ; — thus only was I able to come to you. . . . Be good to our mother."

With these words he stood up, and in the same instant disappeared.

Then Hasébé knew that Akana had killed himself in order to fulfil the promise.

At earliest dawn Hasébé Samon set out for the Castle Tonda, in the province of Izumo. Reaching Matsué, he there learned that, on the night of the ninth day of the ninth month, Akana Soyëmon had performed *harakiri* in the house of Akana Tanji, in the grounds of the castle. Then Hasébé went to the house of Akana Tanji, and reproached Akana Tanji for the treachery done, and slew him in the midst of his family, and escaped without hurt. And when the Lord Tsunéhisa had heard the story, he gave commands that Hasébé should not be pursued. For, although an unscrupulous and cruel man himself, the Lord Tsunéhisa could respect the love of truth in others, and could admire the friendship and the courage of Hasébé Samon.

Of a Promise Broken[1]

I

" I AM not afraid to die," said the dying wife; — "there is only one thing that troubles me now. I wish that I could know who will take my place in this house."

" My dear one," answered the sorrowing husband, " nobody shall ever take your place in my home. I will never, never marry again."

At the time that he said this he was speaking out of his heart; for he loved the woman whom he was about to lose.

" On the faith of a samurai ? " she questioned, with a feeble smile.

" On the faith of a samurai," he responded, — stroking the pale thin face.

" Then, my dear one," she said, " you will let me be buried in the garden, — will you not ? — near those plum-trees that we planted at the

---

[1] Izumo legend.

19

further end? I wanted long ago to ask this; but I thought, that if you were to marry again, you would not like to have my grave so near you. Now you have promised that no other woman shall take my place; — so I need not hesitate to speak of my wish. . . . I want so much to be buried in the garden! I think that in the garden I should sometimes hear your voice, and that I should still be able to see the flowers in the spring."

"It shall be as you wish," he answered. "But do not now speak of burial: you are not so ill that we have lost all hope."

"*I* have," she returned; — "I shall die this morning. . . . But you will bury me in the garden?"

"Yes," he said, — "under the shade of the plum-trees that we planted; — and you shall have a beautiful tomb there."

"And will you give me a little bell?"

"Bell — ?"

"Yes: I want you to put a little bell in the coffin, — such a little bell as the Buddhist pilgrims carry. Shall I have it?"

"You shall have the little bell, — and anything else that you wish."

"I do not wish for anything else," she said. . . . "My dear one, you have been very good to me always. Now I can die happy."

Then she closed her eyes and died — as easily as a tired child falls asleep. She looked beautiful when she was dead; and there was a smile upon her face.

She was buried in the garden, under the shade of the trees that she loved; and a small bell was buried with her. Above the grave was erected a handsome monument, decorated with the family crest, and bearing the kaimyō: — "*Great Elder Sister, Luminous-Shadow-of-the-Plum-Flower-Chamber, dwelling in the Mansion of the Great Sea of Compassion.*"

But, within a twelve-month after the death of his wife, the relatives and friends of the samurai began to insist that he should marry again. "You are still a young man," they said, "and an only son; and you have no children. It is the duty of a samurai to marry. If you die childless, who will there be to make the offerings and to remember the ancestors?"

By many such representations he was at last persuaded to marry again. The bride was only seventeen years old ; and he found that he could love her dearly, notwithstanding the dumb reproach of the tomb in the garden.

II

NOTHING took place to disturb the happiness of the young wife until the seventh day after the wedding, — when her husband was ordered to undertake certain duties requiring his presence at the castle by night. On the first evening that he was obliged to leave her alone, she felt uneasy in a way that she could not explain, — vaguely afraid without knowing why. When she went to bed she could not sleep. There was a strange oppression in the air, — an indefinable heaviness like that which sometimes precedes the coming of a storm.

About the Hour of the Ox she heard, outside in the night, the clanging of a bell, — a Buddhist pilgrim's bell ; — and she wondered what pilgrim could be passing through the samurai quarter at such a time. Presently, after a pause, the bell sounded much nearer. Evidently the pilgrim was approaching the house;—but why approaching from the rear, where no road was? . . . Suddenly the dogs began to whine and howl in an unusual and horrible way;—and a fear came upon her like the fear of dreams. . . . That ringing was certainly in the garden. . . . She tried to get up to waken a servant. But she found that she could not rise,—could not move,—could not call. . . . And nearer, and still more near, came the clang of the bell;—and oh! how the dogs howled! . . . Then, lightly as a shadow steals, there glided into the room a Woman,—though every door stood fast, and every screen unmoved,—a Woman robed in a grave-robe, and carrying a pilgrim's bell. Eyeless she came,—because she had long been dead;—and her loosened hair streamed down about her face;—and she looked without eyes through the tangle of it, and spoke without a tongue:—

" Not in this house,—not in this house shall you stay! Here I am mistress still. You shall go; and you shall tell to none the reason of your going. If you tell HIM, I will tear you into pieces!"

So speaking, the haunter vanished. The bride became senseless with fear. Until the dawn she so remained.

Nevertheless, in the cheery light of day, she doubted the reality of what she had seen and heard. The memory of the warning still weighed upon her so heavily that she did not dare to speak of the vision, either to her husband or to any one else; but she was almost able to persuade herself that she had only dreamed an ugly dream, which had made her ill.

On the following night, however, she could not doubt. Again, at the Hour of the Ox, the dogs began to howl and whine; — again the bell resounded, — approaching slowly from the garden; — again the listener vainly strove to rise and call; — again the dead came into the room, and hissed, —

"You shall go; and you shall tell to no one why you must go! If you even whisper it to HIM, I will tear you in pieces!" . . .

This time the haunter came close to the couch, — and bent and muttered and mowed above it. . . .

Next morning, when the samurai returned from the castle, his young wife prostrated herself before him in supplication : —

"I beseech you," she said, "to pardon my ingratitude and my great rudeness in thus addressing you : but I want to go home ; — I want to go away at once."

"Are you not happy here ? " he asked, in sincere surprise. "Has any one dared to be unkind to you during my absence ? "

"It is not that — " she answered, sobbing. "Everybody here has been only too good to me. . . . But I cannot continue to be your wife ; — I must go away. . . ."

"My dear," he exclaimed, in great astonishment, "it is very painful to know that you have had any cause for unhappiness in this house. But I cannot even imagine why you should want to go away — unless somebody has been very unkind to you. . . . Surely you do not mean that you wish for a divorce ? "

She responded, trembling and weeping, —

"If you do not give me a divorce, I shall die ! "

He remained for a little while silent, — vainly trying to think of some cause for this amazing declaration. Then, without betraying any emotion, he made answer : —

"To send you back now to your people, without any fault on your part, would seem a shameful act. If you will tell me a good reason for your wish, — any reason that will enable me to explain matters honorably, — I can write you a divorce. But unless you give me a reason, a good reason, I will not divorce you, — for the honor of our house must be kept above reproach."

And then she felt obliged to speak ; and she told him everything, — adding, in an agony of terror, —

"Now that I have let you know, she will kill me ! — she will kill me ! . . ."

Although a brave man, and little inclined to believe in phantoms, the samurai was more than startled for the moment. But a simple and natural explanation of the matter soon presented itself to his mind.

"My dear," he said, "you are now very nervous ; and I fear that some one has been telling you foolish stories. I cannot give you a divorce merely because you have had a bad dream in this house. But I am very sorry indeed that you should have been suffering in such a way during my absence. To-night, also, I must be at the castle; but you shall not be alone. I will order two of the retainers to keep watch in your room; and you will be able to sleep in peace. They are good men; and they will take all possible care of you."

Then he spoke to her so considerately and so affectionately that she became almost ashamed of her terrors, and resolved to remain in the house.

III

THE two retainers left in charge of the young wife were big, brave, simple-hearted men, — experienced guardians of women and children. They told the bride pleasant stories to keep her cheerful. She talked with them a long time, laughed at their good-humored fun, and almost forgot her fears. When at last she lay down to sleep, the men-at-arms took their places in a corner of the room, behind a screen, and began a game of go,[1] — speaking only in whispers, that she might not be disturbed. She slept like an infant.

---

[1] A game resembling draughts, but much more complicated.

But again at the Hour of the Ox she awoke with a moan of terror, — for she heard the bell! . . . It was already near, and was coming nearer. She started up; she screamed; — but in the room there was no stir, — only a silence as of death, — a silence growing, — a silence thickening. She rushed to the men-at-arms: they sat before their checker-table, — motionless, — each staring at the other with fixed eyes. She shrieked to them: she shook them: they remained as if frozen. . . .

Afterwards they said that they had heard the bell, — heard also the cry of the bride, — even felt her try to shake them into wakefulness; — and that, nevertheless, they had not been able to move or speak. From the same moment they had ceased to hear or to see: a black sleep had seized upon them.

.   .   .   .   .   .

Entering his bridal-chamber at dawn, the samurai beheld, by the light of a dying lamp, the headless body of his young wife, lying in a pool of blood. Still squatting before their unfinished game, the two retainers slept. At their master's cry they sprang up, and stupidly stared at the horror on the floor. . . .

The head was nowhere to be seen; — and the hideous wound showed that it had not been cut off, but *torn off*. A trail of blood led from the chamber to an angle of the outer gallery, where the storm-doors appeared to have been riven apart. The three men followed that trail into the garden, — over reaches of grass, — over spaces of sand, — along the bank of an iris-bordered pond, — under heavy shadowings of cedar and bamboo. And suddenly, at a turn, they found themselves face to face with a nightmare-thing that chippered like a bat: the figure of the long-buried woman, erect before her tomb, — in one hand clutching a bell, in the other the dripping head. . . . For a moment the three stood numbed. Then one of the men-at-arms, uttering a Buddhist invocation, drew, and struck at the shape. Instantly it crumbled down upon the soil, — an empty scattering of grave-rags, bones, and hair; — and the bell rolled clanking out of the ruin. But the fleshless right hand, though parted from the wrist, still writhed; — and its fingers still gripped at the bleeding head, — and tore, and mangled, — as the claws of the yellow crab cling fast to a fallen fruit. . . .

*
* *

["That is a wicked story," I said to the friend who had related it. "The vengeance of the dead — if taken at all — should have been taken upon the man."

"Men think so," he made answer. "But that is not the way that a woman feels. . . ."

He was right.]

Before the Supreme Court

THE great Buddhist priest, Mongaku Shōnin, says in his book *Kyō-gyō Shin-shō* : — " Many of those gods whom the people worship are unjust gods [*jajin*] : therefore such gods are not worshipped by persons who revere the Three Precious Things.[1] And even persons who obtain favors from those gods, in answer to prayer, usually find at a later day that such favors cause misfortune." This truth is well exemplified by a story recorded in the book *Nihon-Rei-Iki*.

During the time of the Emperor Shōmu[2] there lived in the district called Yamadagori, in the province of Sanuki, a man named Fushiki no Shin.

---

[1] Sambō (Ratnatraya), — the Buddha, the Doctrine, and the Priesthood.

[2] He reigned during the second quarter of the eighth century.

31

He had but one child, a daughter called Kinumé.[1]
Kinumé was a fine-looking girl, and very strong;
but, shortly after she had reached her eighteenth
year, a dangerous sickness began to prevail in that
part of the country, and she was attacked by it.
Her parents and friends then made offerings on
her behalf to a certain Pest-God, and performed
great austerities in honor of the Pest-God, —
beseeching him to save her.

After having lain in a stupor for several days,
the sick girl one evening came to herself, and told
her parents a dream that she had dreamed.   She
had dreamed that the Pest-God appeared to her,
and said: — "Your people have been praying to
me so earnestly for you, and have been worship-
ping me so devoutly, that I really wish to save
you.   But I cannot do so except by giving you
the life of some other person.   Do you happen to
know of any other girl who has the same name
as yours?"   "I remember," answered Kinumé,
"that in Utarigori there is a girl whose name is
the same as mine."   "Point her out to me," the
God said, touching the sleeper; — and at the touch
she rose into the air with him; and, in less than a

------

[1] "Golden Plum-Flower."

second, the two were in front of the house of
the other Kinumé, in Utarigori. It was night;
but the family had not yet gone to bed, and the
daughter was washing something in the kitchen.
"That is the girl," said Kinumé of Yamadagori.
The Pest-God took out of a scarlet bag at his
girdle a long sharp instrument shaped like a chisel;
and, entering the house, he drove the sharp instrument into the forehead of Kinumé of Utarigori. Then Kinumé of Utarigori sank to the
floor in great agony; and Kinumé of Yamadagori awoke, and related the dream.

Immediately after having related it, however,
she again fell into a stupor. For three days she
remained without knowledge of the world; and
her parents began to despair of her recovery.
Then once more she opened her eyes, and spoke.
But almost in the same moment she rose from
her bed, looked wildly about the room, and
rushed out of the house, exclaiming:— "This is
not my home!— you are not my parents!" . . .

Something strange had happened.

Kinumé of Utarigori had died after having
been stricken by the Pest-God. Her parents sor-
rowed greatly; and the priests of their parish-

temple performed a Buddhist service for her ; and
her body was burned in a field outside the village.
Then her spirit descended to the Meido, the world
of the dead, and was summoned to the tribunal
of Emma-Dai-Ō, — the King and Judge of Souls.
But no sooner had the Judge cast eyes upon her
than he exclaimed : — " This girl is the Utarigori-
Kinumé : she ought not to have been brought
here so soon! Send her back at once to the
Shaba-world,[1] and fetch me the other Kinumé, —
the Yamadagori girl ! " Then the spirit of Kinumé of Utarigori made moan before King Emma,
and complained, saying : — " Great Lord, it is
more than three days since I died ; and by this
time my body must have been burned ; and, if
you now send me back to the Shaba-world, what
shall I do ? My body has been changed into ashes
and smoke ; — I shall have no body ! " " Do not
be anxious," the terrible King answered ; — " I am
going to give you the body of Kinumé of Yamadagori, — for her spirit must be brought here to
me at once. You need not fret about the burning of your body : you will find the body of the

---

[1] The Shaba-world (Sahaloka), in common parlance,
signifies the world of men, — the region of human existence.

other Kinumé very much better." And scarcely had he finished speaking when the spirit of Kinumé of Utarigori revived in the body of Kinumé of Yamadagori.

Now when the parents of Kinumé of Yamadagori saw their sick girl spring up and run away, exclaiming, "This is not my home!" — they imagined her to be out of her mind, and they ran after her, calling out: — "Kinumé, where are you going? — wait for a moment, child! you are much too ill to run like that!" But she escaped from them, and ran on without stopping, until she came to Utarigori, and to the house of the family of the dead Kinumé. There she entered, and found the old people; and she saluted them, crying: — "Oh, how pleasant to be again at home! . . . Is it well with you, dear parents?" They did not recognize her, and thought her mad; but the mother spoke to her kindly, asking: — "Where have you come from, child?" "From the Meido I have come," Kinumé made answer. "I am your own child, Kinumé, returned to you from the dead. But I have now another body, mother." And she related all that had happened; and the old people wondered ex-

ceedingly, yet did not know what to believe.
Presently the parents of Kinumé of Yamadagori
also came to the house, looking for their
daughter; and then the two fathers and the two
mothers consulted together, and made the girl repeat her story, and questioned her over and over
again. But she replied to every question in such
a way that the truth of her statements could not be
doubted. At last the mother of the Yamadagori
Kinumé, after having related the strange dream
which her sick daughter had dreamed, said to the
parents of the Utarigori Kinumé: — "We are
satisfied that the spirit of this girl is the spirit of
your child. But you know that her body is the
body of our child; and we think that both families ought to have a share in her. So we would
ask you to agree that she be considered hence-
forward the daughter of both families." To this
proposal the Utarigori parents joyfully consented;
and it is recorded that in after-time Kinumé inherited the property of both households.

"This story," says the Japanese author of the
Bukkyō Hyakkwa Zenshō, "may be found on the
left side of the twelfth sheet of the first volume
of the *Nihon-Rei-Iki*."

The Story of Kwashin Koji[1]

DURING the period of Tenshō [2] there lived, in one of the northern districts of Kyōto, an old man whom the people called Kwashin Koji. He wore a long white beard, and was always dressed like a Shintō priest; but he made his living by exhibiting Buddhist pictures and by preaching Buddhist doctrine. Every fine day he used to go to the grounds of the temple Gion, and there suspend to some tree a large kakémono on which were depicted the punishments of the various hells. This kakémono was so wonderfully painted that all things represented in it seemed to be real; and the old man would

---

[1] Related in the curious old book *Yasō-Kidan*.

[2] The period of Tenshō lasted from 1573 to 1591 (A. D.). The death of the great captain, Oda Nobunaga, who figures in this story, occurred in 1582.

37

discourse to the people crowding to see it, and explain to them the Law of Cause and Effect, — pointing out with a Buddhist staff [*nyoi*], which he always carried, each detail of the different torments, and exhorting everybody to follow the teachings of the Buddha. Multitudes assembled to look at the picture and to hear the old man preach about it; and sometimes the mat which he spread before him, to receive contributions, was covered out of sight by the heaping of coins thrown upon it.

Oda Nobunaga was at that time ruler of Kyōto and of the surrounding provinces. One of his retainers, named Arakawa, during a visit to the temple of Gion, happened to see the picture being displayed there; and he afterwards talked about it at the palace. Nobunaga was interested by Arakawa's description, and sent orders to Kwashin Koji to come at once to the palace, and to bring the picture with him.

When Nobunaga saw the kakémono he was not able to conceal his surprise at the vividness of the work: the demons and the tortured spirits actually appeared to move before his eyes; and he heard voices crying out of the picture; and the blood there represented seemed to be really flowing, — so that he could not help putting out his finger to feel if the painting was wet. But the finger was not stained, — for the paper proved to be perfectly dry. More and more astonished, Nobunaga asked who had made the wonderful picture. Kwashin Koji answered that it had been painted by the famous Oguri Sōtan, [1] — after he had performed the rite of self-purification every day for a hundred days, and practised great austerities, and made earnest prayer for inspiration to the divine Kwannon of Kiyomidzu Temple.

Observing Nobunaga's evident desire to possess the kakémono, Arakawa then asked Kwashin Koji whether he would " offer it up," as a gift to the great lord. But the old man boldly answered: — " This painting is the only object of value that I possess; and I am able to make a little money by showing it to the people. Were I now to present this picture to the lord, I should deprive myself of the only means which I have to make my living. However, if the lord be greatly desirous to

---

[1] Oguri Sōtan was a great religious artist who flourished in the early part of the fifteenth century. He became a Buddhist priest in the later years of his life.

possess it, let him pay me for it the sum of one hundred ryō of gold. With that amount of money I should be able to engage in some profitable business. Otherwise, I must refuse to give up the picture."

Nobunaga did not seem to be pleased at this reply; and he remained silent. Arakawa presently whispered something in the ear of the lord, who nodded assent; and Kwashin Koji was then dismissed, with a small present of money.

But when the old man left the palace, Arakawa secretly followed him, — hoping for a chance to get the picture by foul means. The chance came; for Kwashin Koji happened to take a road leading directly to the heights beyond the town. When he reached a certain lonesome spot at the foot of the hills, where the road made a sudden turn, he was seized by Arakawa, who said to him: — "Why were you so greedy as to ask a hundred ryō of gold for that picture? Instead of a hundred ryō of gold, I am now going to give you one piece of iron three feet long." Then Arakawa drew his sword, and killed the old man, and took the picture.

The next day Arakawa presented the kaké-mono — still wrapped up as Kwashin Koji had wrapped it before leaving the palace — to Oda Nobunaga, who ordered it to be hung up forthwith. But, when it was unrolled, both Nobunaga and his retainer were astounded to find that there was no picture at all — nothing but a blank surface. Arakawa could not explain how the original painting had disappeared ; and as he had been guilty — whether willingly or unwillingly — of deceiving his master, it was decided that he should be punished. Accordingly he was sentenced to remain in confinement for a considerable time.

Scarcely had Arakawa completed his term of imprisonment, when news was brought to him that Kwashin Koji was exhibiting the famous picture in the grounds of Kitano Temple. Arakawa could hardly believe his ears ; but the information inspired him with a vague hope that he might be able, in some way or other, to secure the kakémono, and thereby redeem his recent fault. So he quickly assembled some of his followers, and hurried to the temple ; but when he reached it he was told that Kwashin Koji had gone away.

Several days later, word was brought to Arakawa that Kwashin Koji was exhibiting the picture at Kiyomidzu Temple, and preaching about it to an immense crowd. Arakawa made all haste to Kiyomidzu; but he arrived there only in time to see the crowd disperse, — for Kwashin Koji had again disappeared.

At last one day Arakawa unexpectedly caught sight of Kwashin Koji in a wine-shop, and there captured him. The old man only laughed good-humoredly on finding himself seized, and said: — "I will go with you; but please wait until I drink a little wine." To this request Arakawa made no objection; and Kwashin Koji thereupon drank, to the amazement of the bystanders, twelve bowls of wine. After drinking the twelfth he declared himself satisfied; and Arakawa ordered him to be bound with a rope, and taken to Nobunaga's residence.

In the court of the palace Kwashin Koji was examined at once by the Chief Officer, and sternly reprimanded. Finally the Chief Officer said to him: — "It is evident that you have been deluding people by magical practices; and for this offence alone you deserve to be heavily punished. However, if you will now respectfully offer up that picture to the Lord Nobunaga, we shall this time overlook your fault. Otherwise we shall certainly inflict upon you a very severe punishment."

At this menace Kwashin Koji laughed in a bewildered way, and exclaimed : — " It is not I who have been guilty of deluding people." Then, turning to Arakawa, he cried out : — "You are the deceiver ! You wanted to flatter the lord by giving him that picture ; and you tried to kill me in order to steal it. Surely, if there be any such thing as crime, that was a crime ! As luck would have it, you did not succeed in killing me ; but if you had succeeded, as you wished, what would you have been able to plead in excuse for such an act ? You stole the picture, at all events. The picture that I now have is only a copy. And after you stole the picture, you changed your mind about giving it to Lord Nobunaga ; and you devised a plan to keep it for yourself. So you gave a blank kakémono to Lord Nobunaga ; and, in order to conceal your secret act and purpose, you pretended that I had deceived you by substituting a blank kakémono for the real one. Where the real picture now is, I do not know. You probably do."

At these words Arakawa became so angry that he rushed towards the prisoner, and would have struck him but for the interference of the guards. And this sudden outburst of anger caused the Chief Officer to suspect that Arakawa was not altogether innocent. He ordered Kwashin Koji to be taken to prison for the time being; and he then proceeded to question Arakawa closely. Now Arakawa was naturally slow of speech; and on this occasion, being greatly excited, he could scarcely speak at all; and he stammered, and contradicted himself, and betrayed every sign of guilt. Then the Chief Officer ordered that Arakawa should be beaten with a stick until he told the truth. But it was not possible for him even to seem to tell the truth. So he was beaten with a bamboo until his senses departed from him, and he lay as if dead.

Kwashin Kojī was told in the prison about what had happened to Arakawa; and he laughed. But after a little while he said to the jailer:—"Listen! That fellow Arakawa really behaved like a rascal; and I purposely brought this punishment upon him, in order to correct his evil inclinations. But now please say to the Chief

Officer that Arakawa must have been ignorant of the truth, and that I shall explain the whole matter satisfactorily."

Then Kwashin Koji was again taken before the Chief Officer, to whom he made the following declaration : — " In any picture of real excellence there must be a ghost ; and such a picture, having a will of its own, may refuse to be separated from the person who gave it life, or even from its rightful owner. There are many stories to prove that really great pictures have souls. It is well known that some sparrows, painted upon a sliding-screen [*fusuma*] by Hōgen Yenshin, once flew away, leaving blank the spaces which they had occupied upon the surface. Also it is well known that a horse, painted upon a certain kakémono, used to go out at night to eat grass. Now, in this present case, I believe the truth to be that, inasmuch as the Lord Nobunaga never became the rightful owner of my kakémono, the picture voluntarily vanished from the paper when it was unrolled in his presence. But if you will give me the price that I first asked, — one hundred ryō of gold, — I think that the painting will then reappear, of its own accord, upon the now blank paper. At all events, let us try!

There is nothing to risk, — since, if the picture does not reappear, I shall at once return the money."

On hearing of these strange assertions, Nobu-naga ordered the hundred ryō to be paid, and came in person to observe the result. The kaké-mono was then unrolled before him; and, to the amazement of all present, the painting reappeared, with all its details. But the colors seemed to have faded a little; and the figures of the souls and the demons did not look really alive, as be-fore. Perceiving this difference, the lord asked Kwashin Koji to explain the reason of it; and Kwashin Koji replied: — " The value of the painting, as you first saw it, was the value of a painting beyond all price. But the value of the painting, as you now see it, represents exactly what you paid for it, — one hundred ryō of gold. . . . How could it be otherwise ? " On hearing this answer, all present felt that it would be worse than useless to oppose the old man any further. He was immediately set at liberty; and Arakawa was also liberated, as he had more than expiated his fault by the punishment which he had undergone.

Now Arakawa had a younger brother named
Buichi, — also a retainer in the service of Nobunaga.   Buichi was furiously angry because Arakawa had been beaten and imprisoned; and he
resolved to kill Kwashin Koji.   Kwashin Koji
no sooner found himself again at liberty than he
went straight to a wine-shop, and called for wine.
Buichi rushed after him into the shop, struck him
down, and cut off his head.   Then, taking the
hundred ryō that had been paid to the old man,
Buichi wrapped up the head and the gold together
in a cloth, and hurried home to show them to
Arakawa.   But when he unfastened the cloth he
found, instead of the head, only an empty wine-
gourd, and only a lump of filth instead of the
gold. . . . And the bewilderment of the brothers
was presently increased by the information that
the headless body had disappeared from the wine-
shop, — none could say how or when.

Nothing more was heard of Kwashin Koji
until about a month later, when a drunken man
was found one evening asleep in the gateway of
Lord Nobunaga's palace, and snoring so loud that
every snore sounded like the rumbling of distant
thunder.   A retainer discovered that the drunk-

ard was Kwashin Koji. For this insolent offence,
the old fellow was at once seized and thrown into
the prison. But he did not awake; and in the
prison he continued to sleep without interruption
for ten days and ten nights, — all the while snoring so that the sound could be heard to a great
distance.

About this time, the Lord Nobunaga came to
his death through the treachery of one of his
captains, Akéchi Mitsuhidé, who thereupon
usurped rule. But Mitsuhidé's power endured
only for a period of twelve days.

Now when Mitsuhidé became master of Kyōto,
he was told of the case of Kwashin Koji; and
he ordered that the prisoner should be brought
before him. Accordingly Kwashin Koji was
summoned into the presence of the new lord; but
Mitsuhidé spoke to him kindly, treated him as a
guest, and commanded that a good dinner should
be served to him. When the old man had eaten,
Mitsuhidé said to him: — "I have heard that you
are very fond of wine; — how much wine can
you drink at a single sitting?" Kwashin Koji
answered: — "I do not really know how much;
I stop drinking only when I feel intoxication

coming on." Then the lord set a great wine-cup [1] before Kwashin Koji, and told a servant to fill the cup as often as the old man wished. And Kwashin Koji emptied the great cup ten times in succession, and asked for more; but the servant made answer that the wine-vessel was exhausted. All present were astounded by this drinking-feat; and the lord asked Kwashin Koji, "Are you not yet satisfied, Sir?" "Well, yes," replied Kwashin Koji, "I am somewhat satisfied; — and now, in return for your august kindness, I shall display a little of my art. Be therefore so good as to observe that screen." He pointed to a large eight-folding screen upon which were painted the Eight Beautiful Views of the Lake of Ōmi (*Ōmi-Hakkei*); and everybody looked at the screen. In one of the views the artist had represented, far away on the lake, a man rowing a boat, — the boat occupying, upon the surface of the screen, a space of less than an inch in length. Kwashin

---

[1] The term "bowl" would better indicate the kind of vessel to which the story-teller refers. Some of the so-called cups, used on festival occasions, were very large, — shallow lacquered basins capable of holding considerably more than a quart. To empty one of the largest size, at a draught, was considered to be no small feat.

Koji then waved his hand in the direction of the boat; and all saw the boat suddenly turn, and begin to move toward the foreground of the picture. It grew rapidly larger and larger as it approached; and presently the features of the boatman became clearly distinguishable. Still the boat drew nearer, — always becoming larger, — until it appeared to be only a short distance away. And, all of a sudden, the water of the lake seemed to overflow, — out of the picture into the room; — and the room was flooded; and the spectators girded up their robes in haste, as the water rose above their knees. In the same moment the boat appeared to glide out of the screen, — a real fishing-boat; — and the creaking of the single oar could be heard. Still the flood in the room continued to rise, until the spectators were standing up to their girdles in water. Then the boat came close up to Kwashin Koji; and Kwashin Koji climbed into it; and the boatman turned about, and began to row away very swiftly. And, as the boat receded, the water in the room began to lower rapidly, — seeming to ebb back into the screen. No sooner had the boat passed the apparent foreground of the picture than the room was dry again! But still the painted vessel appeared to glide over the painted water, — retreating further into the distance, and ever growing smaller, — till at last it dwindled to a dot in the offing. And then it disappeared altogether; and Kwashin Koji disappeared with it. He was never again seen in Japan.

The Story of Umétsu Chūbei[1]

❧

UMÉTSU CHŪBEI was a young samurai of great strength and courage. He was in the service of the Lord Tomura Jūdayū, whose castle stood upon a lofty hill in the neighborhood of Yokoté, in the province of Dewa. The houses of the lord's retainers formed a small town at the base of the hill.

Umétsu was one of those selected for night-duty at the castle-gates. There were two night-watches; — the first beginning at sunset and ending at midnight; the second beginning at midnight and ending at sunrise.

Once, when Umétsu happened to be on the second watch, he met with a strange adventure. While ascending the hill at midnight, to take his place on guard, he perceived a woman standing at the last upper turn of the winding road lead-

---

[1] Related in the *Bukkyō-Hyakkwa-Zenshō*.

ing to the castle. She appeared to have a child in her arms, and to be waiting for somebody. Only the most extraordinary circumstances could account for the presence of a woman in that lonesome place at so late an hour; and Umétsu remembered that goblins were wont to assume feminine shapes after dark, in order to deceive and destroy men. He therefore doubted whether the seeming woman before him was really a human being; and when he saw her hasten towards him, as if to speak, he intended to pass her by without a word. But he was too much surprised to do so when the woman called him by name, and said, in a very sweet voice:— "Good Sir Umétsu, to-night I am in great trouble, and I have a most painful duty to perform: will you not kindly help me by holding this baby for one little moment?" And she held out the child to him.

Umétsu did not recognize the woman, who appeared to be very young: he suspected the charm of the strange voice, suspected a supernatural snare, suspected everything;— but he was naturally kind; and he felt that it would be unmanly to repress a kindly impulse through fear of goblins. Without replying, he took the child. "Please hold it till I come back," said the woman: "I shall return in a very little while." "I will hold it," he answered; and immediately the woman turned from him, and, leaving the road, sprang soundlessly down the hill so lightly and so quickly that he could scarcely believe his eyes. She was out of sight in a few seconds.

Umétsu then first looked at the child. It was very small, and appeared to have been just born. It was very still in his hands; and it did not cry at all.

Suddenly it seemed to be growing larger. He looked at it again. . . . No: it was the same small creature; and it had not even moved. Why had he imagined that it was growing larger?

In another moment he knew why; — and he felt a chill strike through him. The child was not growing larger; *but it was growing heavier.* . . . At first it had seemed to weigh only seven or eight pounds: then its weight had gradually doubled — tripled — quadrupled. Now it could not weigh less than fifty pounds; — and still it was getting heavier and heavier. . . . A hundred pounds! — a hundred and fifty! — two hun-

dred ! . . . Umétsu knew that he had been
deluded, — that he had not been speaking with
any mortal woman, — that the child was not
human. But he had made a promise; and a
samurai was bound by his promise. So he kept
the infant in his arms; and it continued to grow
heavier and heavier . . . two hundred and fifty !
— three hundred ! — four hundred pounds ! . . .
What was going to happen he could not imagine; but he resolved not to be afraid, and not
to let the child go while his strength lasted. . . .
Five hundred ! — five hundred and fifty ! — six
hundred pounds ! All his muscles began to
quiver with the strain; — and still the weight
increased. . . . "*Namu Amida Butsu !*" he
groaned — "*Namu Amida Butsu ! — Namu
Amida Butsu !*" Even as he uttered the holy
invocation for the third time, the weight passed
away from him with a shock; and he stood
stupefied, with empty hands, — for the child had
unaccountably disappeared. But almost in the
same instant he saw the mysterious woman returning as quickly as she had gone. Still pant-
ing she came to him; and he then first saw
that she was very fair; — but her brow dripped
with sweat; and her sleeves were bound back

with *tasuki*-cords, as if she had been working hard.

"Kind Sir Umétsu," she said, "you do not know how great a service you have done me. I am the *Ujigami* [1] of this place; and to-night one of my *Ujiko* found herself in the pains of childbirth, and prayed to me for aid. But the labor proved to be very difficult; and I soon saw that, by my own power alone, I might not be able to save her: — therefore I sought for the help of your strength and courage. And the child that I laid in your hands was the child that had not yet been born; and in the time that you first felt the child becoming heavier and heavier, the danger was very great, — for the Gates of Birth were closed. And when you felt the child become so heavy that you despaired of being able to bear the weight much longer, — in that same moment the mother seemed to be dead, and the family wept for her. Then you three times repeated the prayer, *Namu Amida Butsu!* — and the third time that you uttered

---

[1] *Ujigami* is the title given to the tutelary Shintō divinity of a parish or district. All persons living in that parish or district, and assisting in the maintenance of the temple (*miya*) of the deity, are called *Ujiko*.

it the power of the Lord Buddha came to our aid, and the Gates of Birth were opened. . . . And for that which you have done you shall be fitly rewarded. To a brave samurai no gift can be more serviceable than strength : therefore, not only to you, but likewise to your children and to your children's children, great strength shall be given."

And, with this promise, the divinity disappeared.

Umétsu Chūbei, wondering greatly, resumed his way to the castle. At sunrise, on being relieved from duty, he proceeded as usual to wash his face and hands before making his morning prayer. But when he began to wring the towel which had served him, he was surprised to feel the tough material snap asunder in his hands. He attempted to twist together the separated portions ; and again the stuff parted — like so much wet paper. He tried to wring the four thicknesses ; and the result was the same. Presently, after handling various objects of bronze and of iron which yielded to his touch like clay, he understood that he had come into full possession of the great strength prom-

ised, and that he would have to be careful thence-
forward when touching things, lest they should
crumble in his fingers.

On returning home, he made inquiry as to
whether any child had been born in the settle-
ment during the night. Then he learned that
a birth had actually taken place at the very
hour of his adventure, and that the circumstances had been exactly as related to him by
the 'Ujigami.

The children of Umétsu Chūbei inherited their
father's strength. Several of his descendants —
all remarkably powerful men — were still living
in the province of Dewa at the time when this
story was written.

The Story of Kōgi the Priest[1]

NEARLY one thousand years ago there lived
in the famous temple called Miidera, at
Ōtsu[2] in the province of Ōmi, a learned
priest named Kōgi. He was a great artist. He
painted, with almost equal skill, pictures of the
Buddhas, pictures of beautiful scenery, and pictures of animals or birds; but he liked best to
paint fishes. Whenever the weather was fair, and
religious duty permitted, he would go to Lake
Biwa, and hire fishermen to catch fish for him,
without injuring them in any way, so that he
could paint them afterwards as they swam about
in a large vessel of water. After having made

61

pictures of them, and fed them like pets, he
would set them free again, — taking them back
to the lake himself. His pictures of fish at last
became so famous that people travelled from
great distances to see them. But the most wonderful of all his drawings of fish was not drawn
from life, but was made from the memory of a
dream. For one day, as he sat by the lake-side
to watch the fishes swimming, Kōgi had fallen
into a doze, and had dreamed that he was playing
with the fishes under the water. After he awoke,
the memory of the dream remained so clear that
he was able to paint it ; and this painting, which
he hung up in the alcove of his own room in the
temple, he called " Dream-Carp."

Kōgi could never be persuaded to sell any of
his pictures of fish. He was willing to part with
his drawings of landscapes, of birds, or of flowers ;
but he said that he would not sell a picture of
living fish to any one who was cruel enough to
kill or to eat fish. And as the persons who
wanted to buy his paintings were all fish-eaters,
their offers of money could not tempt him.

One summer Kōgi fell sick ; and after a week's
illness he lost all power of speech and movement,

so that he seemed to be dead. But after his funeral service had been performed, his disciples discovered some warmth in the body, and decided to postpone the burial for awhile, and to keep watch by the seeming corpse. In the afternoon of the same day he suddenly revived, and questioned the watchers, asking: —

"How long have I remained without knowledge of the world?"

"More than three days," an acolyte made answer. "We thought that you were dead; and this morning your friends and parishioners assembled in the temple for your funeral service. We performed the service; but afterwards, finding that your body was not altogether cold, we put off the burial; and now we are very glad that we did so."

Kōgi nodded approvingly: then he said: —

"I want some one of you to go immediately to the house of Taira no Suké, where the young men are having a feast at the present moment — (they are eating fish and drinking wine), — and say to them: — 'Our master has revived; and he begs that you will be so good as to leave your feast, and to call upon him without delay, because he has a wonderful story to tell you.' . . .

At the same time " — continued Kōgi — " observe what Suké and his brothers are doing; — see whether they are not feasting as I say."

Then an acolyte went at once to the house of Taira no Suké, and was surprised to find that Suké and his brother Jūrō, with their attendant, Kamori, were having a feast, just as Kōgi had said. But, on receiving the message, all three immediately left their fish and wine, and hastened to the temple. Kōgi, lying upon the couch to which he had been removed, received them with a smile of welcome; and, after some pleasant words had been exchanged, he said to Suké : —

" Now, my friend, please reply to some questions that I am going to ask you. First of all, kindly tell me whether you did not buy a fish to-day from the fisherman Bunshi."

" Why, yes," replied Suké — " but how did you know ? "

" Please wait a moment," said the priest. . . . " That fisherman Bunshi to-day entered your gate, with a fish three feet long in his basket: it was early in the afternoon, just after you and Jūrō had begun a game of *go;* — and Kamori was watching the game, and eating a peach — was he not ? "

"That is true," exclaimed Suké and Kamori together, with increasing surprise.

"And when Kamori saw that big fish," proceeded Kōgi, "he agreed to buy it at once; and, besides paying the price of the fish, he also gave Bunshi some peaches, in a dish, and three cups of wine. Then the cook was called; and he came and looked at the fish, and admired it; and then, by your order, he sliced it and prepared it for your feast. . . . Did not all this happen just as I have said?"

"Yes," responded Suké; "but we are very much astonished that you should know what happened in our house to-day. Please tell us how you learned these matters."

"Well, now for my story," said the priest. "You are aware that almost everybody believed me to be dead;—you yourselves attended my funeral service. But I did not think, three days ago, that I was at all dangerously ill: I remember only that I felt weak and very hot, and that I wanted to go out into the air to cool myself. And I thought that I got up from my bed, with a great effort, and went out,—supporting myself with a stick. . . . Perhaps this may have been imagination; but you will presently be able to judge the truth for yourselves: I am going to relate everything exactly as it appeared to happen. . . . As soon as I got outside of the house, into the bright air, I began to feel quite light, — light as a bird flying away from the net or the basket in which it has been confined. I wandered on and on till I reached the lake; and the water looked so beautiful and blue that I felt a great desire to have a swim. I took off my clothes, and jumped in, and began to swim about; and I was astonished to find that I could swim very fast and very skilfully, — although before my sickness I had always been a very poor swimmer. . . . You think that I am only telling you a foolish dream — but listen! . . . While I was wondering at this new skill of mine, I perceived many beautiful fishes swimming below me and around me; and I felt suddenly envious of their happiness, — reflecting that, no matter how good a swimmer a man may become, he never can enjoy himself under the water as a fish can. Just then, a very big fish lifted its head above the surface in front of me, and spoke to me with the voice of a man, saying: — 'That wish of yours can very easily be satisfied: please wait there a moment!' The fish then went down, out of sight; and I waited. After a few minutes there came up, from the bottom of the lake, — riding on the back of the same big fish that had spoken to me, — a man wearing the headdress and the ceremonial robes of a prince; and the man said to me: — 'I come to you with a message from the Dragon-King, who knows of your desire to enjoy for a little time the condition of a fish. As you have saved the lives of many fish, and have always shown compassion to living creatures, the God now bestows upon you the attire of the Golden Carp, so that you will be able to enjoy the pleasures of the Water-World. But you must be very careful not to eat any fish, or any food prepared from fish, — no matter how nice may be the smell of it; — and you must also take great care not to get caught by the fishermen, or to hurt your body in any way.' With these words, the messenger and his fish went below and vanished in the deep water. I looked at myself, and saw that my whole body had become covered with scales that shone like gold; — I saw that I had fins; — I found that I had actually been changed into a Golden Carp. Then I knew that I could swim wherever I pleased.

" Thereafter it seemed to me that I swam away, and visited many beautiful places. [*Here, in the original narrative, are introduced some verses describing the Eight Famous Attractions of the Lake of Ōmi, — " Ōmi-Hakkei."*] Sometimes I was satisfied only to look at the sunlight dancing over the blue water, or to admire the beautiful reflection of hills and trees upon still surfaces sheltered from the wind. . . . I remember especially the coast of an island — either Okitsushima or Chikubushima — reflected in the water like a red wall. . . . Sometimes I would approach the shore so closely that I could see the faces and hear the voices of people passing by ; sometimes I would sleep on the water until startled by the sound of approaching oars. At night there were beautiful moonlight-views ; but I was frightened more than once by the approaching torchfires of the fishing-boats of Katasé. When the weather was bad, I would go below, — far down, — even a thousand feet, — and play at the bottom of the lake. But after two or three days of this wandering pleasure, I began to feel very hungry ; and I returned to this neighborhood in the hope of finding something to eat. Just at that time the fisherman Bunshi happened to be fishing; and I approached the hook which he had let down into the water. There was some fish-food upon it that was good to smell. I remembered in the same moment the warning of the Dragon-King, and swam away, saying to myself: — 'In any event I must not eat food containing fish; — I am a disciple of the Buddha.' Yet after a little while my hunger became so intense that I could not resist the temptation; and I swam back again to the hook, thinking, — ' Even if Bunshi should catch me, he would not hurt me; — he is my old friend.' I was not able to loosen the bait from the hook; and the pleasant smell of the food was too much for my patience; and I swallowed the whole thing at a gulp. Immediately after I did so, Bunshi pulled in his line, and caught me. I cried out to him, ' What are you doing? — you hurt me! ' — but he did not seem to hear me, and he quickly put a string through my jaws. Then he threw me into his basket, and took me to your house. When the basket was opened there, I saw you and Jūrō playing *go* in the south room, and Kamori watching you — eating a peach the while. All of you presently came out upon the veranda to look at me; and you were delighted to see

such a big fish. I called out to you as loud as I
could : — 'I am not a fish ! — I am Kōgi — Kōgi
the priest ! please let me go back to my temple ! '
But you clapped your hands for gladness, and
paid no attention to my words. Then your cook
carried me into the kitchen, and threw me down
violently upon a cutting-board, where a terribly
sharp knife was lying. With his left hand he
pressed me down, and with his right hand he
took up that knife, — and I screamed to him : —
'How can you kill me so cruelly ! I am a disciple of the Buddha ! — help ! help ! ' But in the
same instant I felt his knife dividing me — a
frightful pain ! — and then I suddenly awoke, and
found myself here in the temple."

When the priest had thus finished his story,
the brothers wondered at it ; and Suké said to
him : — " I now remember noticing that the jaws
of the fish were moving all the time that we were
looking at it ; but we did not hear any voice. . . .
Now I must send a servant to the house with
orders to throw the remainder of that fish into
the lake."

Kōgi soon recovered from his illness, and lived
to paint many more pictures. It is related that,

long after his death, some of his fish-pictures once happened to fall into the lake, and that the figures of the fish immediately detached themselves from the silk or the paper upon which they had been painted, and swam away!

FOLKLORE GLEANINGS

Dragon-flies

1

ONE of the old names of Japan is *Akitsu-shima,* meaning "The Island of the Dragon-fly," and written with the character representing a dragon-fly, — which insect, now called *tombō,* was anciently called *akitsu.* Perhaps this name Akitsushima, "Island of the Dragon-fly," was phonetically suggested by a still older name for Japan, also pronounced *Akitsushima,* but written with different characters, and signifying "The Land of Rich Harvests." However this may be, there is a tradition that the Emperor Jimmu, some twenty-six hundred years ago, ascended a mountain to gaze over the province of Yamato, and observed to those who accompanied him that the configuration of the land was like a dragon-fly licking its tail. Because of this august observation the province of Yamato came to be known as the Land of the Dragon-fly; and eventually the name was extended to the whole island. And the Dragon-fly remains an emblem of the Empire even to this day.

In a literal sense, Japan well deserves to be called the Land of the Dragon-fly; for, as Rein poetically declared, it is "a true Eldorado to the neuroptera-fancier." Probably no other country of either temperate zone possesses so many kinds of dragon-flies; and I doubt whether even the tropics can produce any dragon-flies more curiously beautiful than some of the Japanese species. The most wonderful dragon-fly that I ever saw was a Japanese *Calepteryx,* which I captured last summer in Shidzuoka. It was what the country-folk call a "black dragon-fly"; but the color was really a rich deep purple. The long narrow wings, velvety purple, seemed — even to touch — like the petals of some marvellous flower. The purple body, slender as a darning-needle, was decorated with dotted lines of dead gold. The head and thorax were vivid gold-green; but the eyes were pure globes of burnished gold. The legs were fringed on the inner side with indescribably delicate spines, set at right angles to the limb, like the teeth of a fairy-comb. So exquisite was the creature that I felt a kind of remorse for having disturbed it, — felt as if I had been meddling with something belonging to the gods; — and I quickly returned it to the shrub on which it had been reposing. . . . This particular kind of dragon-fly is said to haunt only the neighborhood of a clear stream near the town of Yaidzu. It is, however, but one of many lovely varieties.

But the more exquisite dragon-flies are infrequently seen; and they seldom figure in Japanese literature; — and I can attempt to interest my reader only in the poetry and the folklore of dragon-flies. I propose to discourse of dragon-flies in the old-fashioned Japanese way; and the little that I have been able to learn upon the subject, — with the help of quaint books and of long-forgotten drawings, — mostly relates to the commoner species.

But before treating of dragon-fly literature, it will be necessary to say something regarding dragon-fly nomenclature. Old Japanese books profess to name about fifty kinds; and the *Chūfu-*

Zusétsu actually contains colored pictures of
nearly that number of dragon-flies. But in these
volumes several insects resembling dragon-flies are
improperly classed with dragon-flies; and in more
than one case it would seem that different names
have been given to the male and female of the
same species. On the other hand I find as many
as four different varieties of dragon-fly bearing
the same folk-name! And in view of these facts
I venture to think that the following list will be
found sufficiently complete :—

I. — *Mugiwara-tòmbō* (or simply, *tombō*),
" Barley-straw Dragon-fly," — so called because
its body somewhat resembles in shape and color a
barley-straw. — This is perhaps the most common
of all the dragon-flies, and the first to make its
appearance.

II. — *Shiokara-tombō,* or *Shio-tombō,* —" Salt-
fish Dragon-fly;" or " Salt Dragon-fly," — so
called because the end of its tail looks as if it
had been dipped in salt. *Shiokara* is the name
given to a preparation of fish preserved in salt.

III. — *Kino-tombō,* " Yellow Dragon-fly." — It
is not all yellow, but reddish, with yellow stripes
and bands.

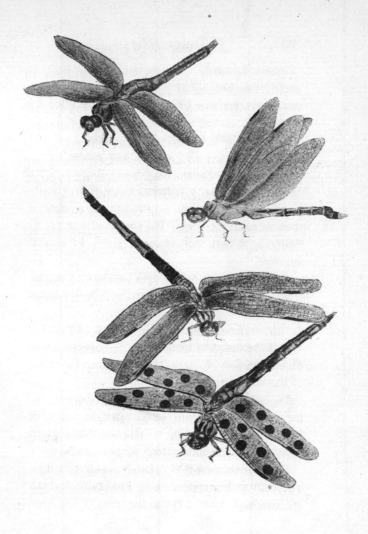

Dragon-flies (top to bottom): *Shio-Tombō*; *Mugiwara-Tombō*; *Kino-Tombō*; *Ko-Mugi-Tombō*.

IV. — *Aɔ-tombō*. *Ao* means either blue or green; and two different kinds of dragon-fly, — one green, and one metallic-blue, — are called by this name.

V. — *Koshiaki-tombō*, — "Shining Loins." The insect usually so called is black and yellow.

VI. — *Tono - Sama - tombō*, — "August - Lord Dragon-fly." Many different kinds of dragon-fly are called by this name, — probably on account of their beautiful colors. The name *Koshiaki*, or "Shining Loins," is likewise given to several varieties.

VII. — *Ko-mugi-tombō*, "Wheat-straw Dragon-fly." — Somewhat smaller than the "Barley-straw dragon-fly."

VIII. — *Tsumaguro-tombō*, "Black-skirted (or "black-hemmed") Dragon-fly." — Several kinds of dragon-flies are thus called, because the edges of the wings are black or dark-red.

IX. — *Kuro-tombō*, "Black Dragon-fly." As the word *kuro* means either dark in color or black, it is not surprising to find this name given both to deep red and to deep purple insects.

X.—*Karakasa-tombō*, "Umbrella Dragon-fly." The body of this creature is said to resemble, both in form and color, a closed umbrella of the kind known as *karakasa,* made of split bamboo covered with thick oil-paper.

XI. — *Chō-tombō,* — "Butterfly Dragon-fly." Several varieties of dragon-fly are thus called, — apparently because of wing-markings like those of moths or butterflies.

XII. — *Shōjō-tombō.* A bright-red dragon-fly is so named, simply because of its tint. — In the zoölogical mythology of China and Japan, the *Shōjō* figures as a being less than human, but more than animal, — in appearance resembling a stout boy with long crimson hair. From this crimson hair it was alleged that a wonderful red dye could be extracted. The *Shōjō* was supposed to be very fond of *saké;* and in Japanese art the creature is commonly represented as dancing about a *saké*-vessel.

XIII.—*Haguro-tombō,* "Black-winged Dragon-fly."

XIV. — *Oni - yamma,* "Demon Dragon-fly." This is the largest of all the Japanese dragon-flies. It is rather unpleasantly colored; the body being black, with bright yellow bands and stripes.

XV. — *Ki-yamma,* "Goblin Dragon-fly." Also called *Ki-Emma,* — "Emma," or " *Yemma,*" being

Dragon-flies (top to bottom): *Yurei-Tombō; Yuro Tombō;*
Shoiō-Tombō; Kane-tsuke-Tombō.

the name of the King of Death and Judge of Souls.

XVI. — *Shōryō-tombō,* " The Dragon-fly of the Ancestral Spirits." This appellation, as well as another of kindred meaning, — *Shōrai-tombō,* or " Dragon-fly of the Dead," — would appear, so far as I could learn, to be given to many kinds of dragon-fly.

XVII. — *Yurei-tombō,* — " Ghost Dragon-fly." Various creatures are called by this name, — which I thought especially appropriate in the case of one beautiful *Calepteryx,* whose soundless black flitting might well be mistaken for the motion of a shadow, — the shadow of a dragon-fly. Indeed this appellation for the black insect must have been intended to suggest the primitive idea of shadow as ghost.

XVIII. — *Kané-tsuké - tombō,* or *O-haguro - tombō.* Either name refers to the preparation formerly used to blacken the teeth of married women, and might be freely rendered as " Tooth-blackening Dragon-fly." *O-haguro* (" honorable tooth-blackening ") or *Kané,* were the terms by which the tooth-staining infusion was commonly known. *Kané wo tsukéru* signified to apply, or, more literally, *to wear* the stuff : thus

the appellation *Kané-tsuké tombō* might be interpreted as "the *Kané*-stained Dragon-fly." The
wings of the insect are half-black, and look as if
they had been partly dipped in ink. Another
and equally picturesque name for the creature is
Kōya, "the Dyer."

XIX. — *Ta-no-Kami-tombō,* "Dragon-fly of
the God of Rice-fields." This appellation has
been given to an insect variegated with red and
yellow.

XX. — *Yanagi-jorō,* "The Lady of the Weep-
ing-willow." A beautiful, but ghostly name;
for the *Yanagi-jorō* is the Spirit of the Willow-
tree. I find that two very graceful species of
dragon-fly are thus called.

XXI. — *Seki-i-Shisha,* "Red-robed Messenger."

XXII. — *Yamma-tombō.* The name is a sort
of doublet; *yamma* signifying a large dragon-fly,
and *tombō* any sort of dragon-fly. This is the
name for a black-and-green insect, called *Onjō*
in Izumo.

XXIII. — *Kuruma-yamma,* "Wagon Dragon-
fly," — probably so-named from the disk-like
appendages of the tail.

XXIV. — *Aka-tombō,* "Red Dragon-fly." The
name is now given to various species; but the

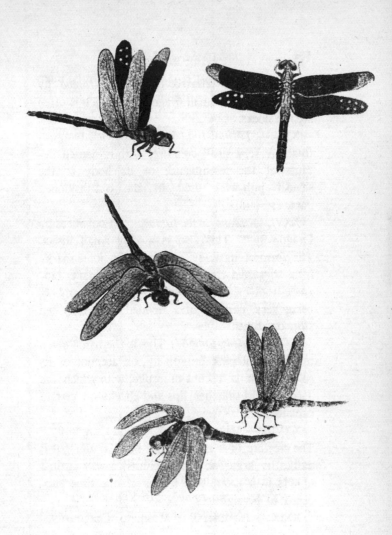

Dragon-flies: (top) *Haguro-Tombō* (two views); (middle)
Seki-I-Shisha; (bottom) *Aka-Tombō* (two views).

insect especially referred to as *Aka-tombō* by the old poets is a small dragon-fly, which is often seen in flocks.

XXV. — *Tōsumi-tombō,* " Lamp-wick Dragon-fly." A very small creature, — thus named because of the resemblance of its body to the slender pith-wick used in the old-fashioned Japanese lamp.

XXVI. — *Mono-sashi-tombō,* " Foot-measure Dragon-fly." This also is a very small insect. The form of its body, with the ten joint-markings, suggested this name ; — the ordinary Japanese foot-measure, usually made of bamboo, being very narrow, and divided into only ten *sun*, or inches.

XXVII. — *Beni-tombō.* This is the name given to a beautiful pink dragon-fly, on account of its color. *Beni* is a kind of rouge, with which the Japanese girl tints her lips and cheeks on certain occasions.

XXVIII. — *Mékura-tombō,* " Blind Dragon-fly." The creature thus called is not blind at all ; but it dashes its large body in so clumsy a way against objects in a room that it was at one time supposed to be sightless.

XXIX. — *Ka-tombō,* " Mosquito Dragon-fly,"

— perhaps in the same sense as the American term " mosquito-hawk."

XXX. — *Kuro-yama-tombō,* "Black Mountain-Dragon-fly," — so called to distinguish it from the *Yama-tombō,* or " Mountain Dragon-fly," which is mostly green.

XXXI. — *Ko-yama-tombō,* " Little Mountain-Dragon-fly," — the name of a small insect resembling the *Yama-tombō* in form and color.

XXXII. — *Tsukété-dan.* The word *dan* is a general term for variegated woven stuffs; and the name *tsukété-dan* might be freely rendered as " The Wearer of the Many-Colored Robe."

I believe that in the foregoing list the only name requiring further explanation is the name *Shōrai-tombō,* or *Shōryō-tombō,* in its meaning of " the Dragon-fly of the Dead." Unlike the equally weird name *Yurei-tombō,* or " Ghost Dragon-fly," the term *Shōrai-tombō* does not refer to the appearance of the insect, but to the strange belief that certain dragon-flies *are ridden by the dead,* — used as winged steeds. From the morning of the thirteenth to the midnight of the fifteenth day of the old seventh month, — the time of the Festival of the Bon, — the dragon-flies are said to carry the *Hotoké-Sama,* the August Spirits of the Ancestors, who then revisit their former homes. Therefore during this Buddhist "All-Souls," children are forbidden to molest any dragon-flies, — especially dragon-flies that may then happen to enter the family dwelling. This supposed relation of dragon-flies to the supernatural world helps to explain an old folk saying, still current in some provinces, to the effect that the child who catches dragon-flies will never "obtain knowledge." Another curious belief is that certain dragon-flies "carry the image of Kwannon-Sama (Âvalokitesvara)," — because the markings upon the backs of the insects bear some faint resemblance to the form of a Buddhist icon.

II

DIFFERENT kinds of dragon-fly show themselves at different periods; and the more beautiful species, with few exceptions, are the latest to appear. All Japanese dragon-flies have been grouped by old writers into four classes, according to the predominant color of each variety, — the Yellow, Green (or Blue), Black (or Dark), and Red

Dragon-flies. It is said that the yellow-marked insects are the earliest to appear; that the green, blue, and black varieties first show themselves in the Period of Greatest Heat; and that the red kinds are the last to come and the last to go, — vanishing only with the close of autumn. In a vague and general way, these statements can be accepted as results of observation. Nevertheless, the dragon-fly is popularly spoken of as a creature of autumn: indeed one of its many names, *Akitsu-mushi*, signifies " autumn insect." And the appellation is really appropriate; for it is not until the autumn that dragon-flies appear in such multitude as to compel attention. For the poet, however, the true dragon-fly of autumn is the red dragon-fly:

> Aki no ki no
> Aka-tombō ni
> Sadamarinu.

That the autumn season has begun is decided by the [*appearance of the*] red dragon-fly.

> Onoga mi ni
> Aki wo sonémuku
> Tombō kana!

O the dragon-fly! — he has dyed his own body with [*the color of*] autumn!

Dragon-flies

Aki no hi no
Sométa iro nari
Aka-tombō !

Dyed he is with the color of autumn days — O the red
dragon-fly !

"Spring," says a Japanese poet, "is the Season
of the Eyes ; Autumn is the Season of the Ears,"
— meaning that in spring the blossoming of the
trees and the magic of morning haze make delight for the eyes, and that in autumn the ears
are charmed by the music of countless insects.
But he goes on to say that this pleasure of
autumn is toned with melancholy. Those plain-
tive voices evoke the memory of vanished years
and of vanished faces, and so to Buddhist
thought recall the doctrine of impermanency·
Spring is the period of promise and of hope ;
autumn, the time of remembrance and of regret.
And the coming of autumn's special insect, the
soundless dragon-fly, — voiceless in the season
of voices, — only makes weirder the aspects of
change. Everywhere you see a silent play of
fairy lightnings, — flashes of color continually
intercrossing, like a weaving of interminable

enchantment over the face of the land. Thus
an old poet describes it: —

> Kurénai no
> Kagerō hashiru,
> Tombō kana!

Like a fleeting of crimson gossamer-threads, the flashing
of the dragon-flies.

III

FOR more than ten centuries the Japanese have
been making verses about dragon-flies · and the
subject remains a favorite one even with the
younger poets of to-day. The oldest extant
poem about a dragon-fly is said to have been
composed, fourteen hundred and forty years
ago, by the Emperor Yūriaku. One day while
this Emperor was hunting, say the ancient
records, a gadfly came and bit his arm. Therewith a dragon-fly pounced upon that gadfly,
and devoured it. Then the Emperor commanded his ministers to make an ode in praise
of that dragon-fly. But as they hesitated how
to begin, he himself composed a poem in praise
of the insect, ending with the words, —

"Even a creeping insect
Waits upon the Great Lord:
Thy form it will bear,
O Yamato, land of the dragon-fly!"

And in honor of the loyal dragon-fly, the place
of the incident was called *Akitsuno*, or the Moor
of the Dragon-fly.

The poem attributed to the Emperor Yūriaku
is written in the form called *naga-uta,* or "long-
poetry"; but the later poems on dragon-flies
are mostly composed in the briefer forms of
Japanese verse.   There are three brief forms, —
the ancient *tanka,* consisting of thirty-one syllables; the popular *dodoitsu,* consisting of twenty-
six syllables; and the *hokku,* consisting of only
seventeen.   The vast majority of dragon-fly
poems are in *hokku.*   There are scarcely any
poems upon the subject in *dodoitsu,* and —
strange to say! — but very few in the classical
tanka.   The friend who collected for me all
the verses quoted in this essay, and many hundreds more, declares that he read through *fifty-
two volumes* of thirty-one-syllable poetry in
the Imperial Library before he succeeded in
finding a single composition about dragon-flies;

and eventually, after much further research, he was able to discover only about a dozen such poems in *tanka*.

The reason for this must be sought in the old poetical conventions. Japanese thirty-one-syllable poetry is composed according to rules that have been fixed for hundreds of years. These rules require that almost every subject treated shall be considered in some relation to one of the seasons. And this should be done in accordance with certain laws of grouping, — long-established conventions of association, recognized both in painting and in poetry: for example, the nightingale should be mentioned, or por-trayed, together with the plum-tree; the sparrow, with the bamboo; the cuckoo, with the moon; frogs, with rain; the butterfly, with flowers; the bat, with the willow-tree. Every Japanese child knows something about these regulations. Now, it so happens that no such relations have been clearly fixed for the dragon-fly in *tanka*-poetry, — though in pictures we often see it perched on the edge of a water-bucket, or upon an ear of ripened rice. Moreover, in the classification of subject-groupings for poetry, the dragon-fly is not placed among *mushi* (" insects " — by

which word the poet nearly always means a
musical insect of some sort), but among zō, —
a term of very wide signification; for it includes
the horse, cat, dog, monkey, crow, sparrow, tor-
toise, snake, frog, — almost all fauna, in short.

Thus the rarity of *tanka*-poems about dragon-
flies may be explained. But why should dragon-
flies be almost ignored in *dodoitsu?* Probably
for the reason that this form of verse is usually
devoted to the subject of love. The voiceless
dragon-fly can suggest to the love-poet no such
fancies as those inspired by the singing-insects, —
especially by those night-crickets whose music
lingers in the memory of some evening tryst.
Out of several hundred dragon-fly poems collected for me, I find only seven relating, directly
or indirectly, to the subject of love; and not one
of the seven is in twenty-six-syllable verse.

But in the form *hokku* — limited to seventeen
syllables — the poems on dragon-flies are almost
as numerous as are the dragon-flies themselves
in the early autumn. For in this measure there
are few restraints placed upon the composer,
either as to theme or method. Almost the only
rule about *hokku*, — not at all a rigid one, — is
that the poem shall be a little word-picture, —

that it shall revive the memory of something seen or felt, — that it shall appeal to some experience of sense. The greater number of the poems that I am going to quote certainly fulfil this requirement: the reader will find that they are really pictures, — tiny color-prints in the manner of the *Ukiyo-yé* school. Indeed almost any of the following could be delightfully imaged, with a few touches of the brush, by some Japanese master : —

PICTURE-POEMS ABOUT DRAGON-FLIES

Iné no ho no
Tombō tomari
Tarénikéri.

An ear of rice has bent because a dragon-fly perched upon it.

Tombō no
Éda ni tsuitari
Wasuré-guwa.

See the dragon-fly resting on the handle of the forgotten mattock.[1]

---

[1] The *kuwa* is shaped like a hoe, but is a much heavier tool. When left with the heavy blade resting flat upon the ground, as suggested in this little word-picture, the handle remains almost perpendicular.

Tombō no
Kaidé yukikéri
Suté waraji.

Dragon-flies have gone to sniff at a pair of cast-off
sandals of straw.

Sodé ni tsuku
Sumi ka? — obana ni
Kané-tombō!

Is it an ink-stain upon a sleeve? — no: it is only the
black dragon-fly resting upon the *obana*.[1]

Hi wa namamé
Sékiya no yari ni
Tombō kana!

See the dragon-fly perching on the blade of the spear
leaning against the rampart-wall!

Tombō no
Kusa ni undéya,
Ushi no tsuno!

O dragon-fly! how have you wearied of the grass that
you should thus perch upon the horn of a cow!

---

[1] *Obana* is another name for the beautiful flowering grass usually
called *susuki*, and known to botanists as *Eularia Japonica*.

Kaki-daké no
Ippon nagaki —
Tombō kana !

One of the bamboo-stakes in that fence seems to be
higher than the others — but no! there is a dragon-fly
upon it !

Kaki-daké to
Tombō to utsuru
Shōji kana !

The shadow of the bamboo-fence, with a dragon-fly at
rest upon it, is thrown upon my paper-window !

Tsurigané ni
Hito-toki yasumi
Tombō kana !

See! the dragon-fly is resting awhile upon the temple-
bell !

O wo motté
Kané ni mukaëru, —
Tombō kana !

Only with his tail he thinks to oppose [*the weight of*]
the great temple-bell, — O silly dragon-fly !

Naki-hito no
Shirushi no také ni
Tombō kana !

Lo ! a dragon-fly rests upon the bamboo that marks the grave !

Itté wa kité
Tombō taëzu
Funé no tsuna.

About the ropes of the ship the dragon-flies cease not to come and go.

Tombō ya
Funé wa nagarété
Todomarazu.

The dragon-fly ceases not to flit about the vessel drifting down the stream.

Tombō ya !
Hobashira até ni
Tōku yuku.

O the dragon-fly ! — keeping an eye upon the mast, he ventures far !

Tombō ya !
Hi no kagé dékité,
Nami no uĕ.

Poor dragon-fly ! — now that the sun has become obscured, he wanders over the waves.

Wata-tori no
Kasa ya tombō no
Hitotsu-zutsu.

Look at the bamboo-hats of the cotton-pickers ! — there
is a dragon-fly perched on each of them !

Nagaré-yuku
Awa ni yumé mñu
Tombō kana !

Lo ! the dragon-fly dreams a dream above the flowing
of the foam-bubbles !

Uki-kusa no
Hana ni asobu ya,
Aka-tombō !

See the red dragon-fly sporting about the blossoms of
the water-weed !

Tombō no
Hitoshio akashi
Fuchi no uĕ.

Much more red seems the red dragon-fly when hovering
above the pool.

Tsuri-béta no
Sao ni kité néru
Tombō kana !

See ! the dragon-fly settles down to sleep on the rod of
the unskilful angler !

Dragon-flies

Tombō no
Ha-ura ni sabishi, —
Aki-shiguré.

Lonesomely clings the dragon-fly to the underside of the leaf — Ah! the autumn-rains!

Tombō no
Tō bakari tsuku
Kara-é kana!

Only ten dragon-flies — all clinging to the same withered spray!

Yosogoto no
Naruko ni nigéru,
Tombō kana!

Poor dragon-fly! scared away by the clapper[1] that never was intended for you!

Aŏ-zora ya,
Ka hodo muré-tobu
Aka-tombō.

High in the azure sky the gathering of red dragon-flies looks like a swarming of mosquitoes.

---

[1] *Naruko.* This clapper, used to frighten away birds from the crops, consists of a number of pieces of bamboo, or hard wood, fastened to a rope extended across the field or garden. When the end of the rope is pulled, the pieces of wood rattle loudly.

Furú-haka ya ;
Aka-tombō tobu ;
Karé shikimi.

Old tomb ! — [*only*] a flitting of red dragon-flies ; — some
withered [*offerings of*] shikimi [1] [*before the grave*] !

Sabishisa wo !
Tombō tobu nari
Haka no uĕ.

Desolation ! — dragon-flies flitting above the graves !

Tombō tondé,
Koto-naki mura no
Hi go nari.

Dragon-flies are flitting, and the noon-sun is shining,
above the village where nothing eventful ever happens.

Yūzuki hi
Usuki tombō no
Ha-kagé kana !

O the thin shadow of the dragon-fly's wings in the light
of sunset !

---

[1] It is the custom to set sprays of *shikimi* in bamboo vases before
the graves of Buddhist dead. This *shikimi* is a kind of anise, botani-
cally known as *Illicium religiosum.*

Tombō no
Kabé wo kakayuru
Nishi-hi kana!

O that sunlight from the West, and the dragon-fly clinging to the wall!

Tombō toru
Iri-hi ni tori no
Métsuki kana!

O the expression of that cock's eyes in the sunset-light
— trying to catch a dragon-fly!

Tombō no
Mō ya iri-hi no
Issékai.

Dance, O dragon-flies, in your world of the setting sun!

Nama-kabé ni
Yū-hi sasunari
Aka-tombō.

To the freshly-plastered wall a red dragon-fly clings in
the light of the setting-sun.[1]

---

[1] This is a tiny color-study. The tint of the freshly-plastered wall
is supposed to be a warm grey.

Déru tsuki to
Iri-hi no ai ya —
Aka-tombō.

In the time between the setting of the sun and the rising
of the moon — red dragon-flies.

Yū-kagé ya,
Nagaré ni hitasu
Tombō no o!

The dragon-fly at dusk dips her tail into the running
stream.

IV

THE foregoing compositions are by old authors
mostly: few modern hokku on the subject have
the same naïve quality of picturesqueness. The
older poets seem to have watched the ways of
the dragon-fly with a patience and a freshness of
curiosity impossible to this busier generation.
They made verses about all its habits and pecu-
liarities, — even about such matters as the queer
propensity of the creature to return many times
in succession to any spot once chosen for a perch.
Sometimes they praised the beauty of its wings,

and compared them to the wings of devas or
Buddhist angels; sometimes they celebrated the
imponderable grace of its hovering, — the ghostly
stillness and lightness of its motion; and sometimes they jested about its waspish appearance
of anger, or about the goblin oddity of its stare.
They noticed the wonderful way in which it can
change the direction of its course, or reverse the
play of its wings with the sudden turn that suggested the modern Japanese word for a somersault, — *tombogaëri* ("dragon-fly-turning").[1] In
the dazzling rapidity of its flight — invisible but
as a needle-gleam of darting color — they found
a similitude for impermanency. But they perceived that this lightning flight was of short
duration, and that the dragon-fly seldom travels
far, unless pursued, preferring to flit about one
spot all day long. Some thought it worth while
to record in verse that at sunset all the dragon-
flies flock towards the glow, and that they rise
high in air when the sun sinks below the horizon,
— as if they hoped to obtain from the altitudes
one last sight of the vanishing splendor. They

---

[1] *Tombogaëri wo utsu,* " to throw a dragon-fly-turning "
is the Japanese expression corresponding with our phrase,
" to turn a somersault."

remarked that the dragon-fly cares nothing for flowers, and is apt to light upon stakes or stones rather than upon blossoms; and they wondered what pleasure it could find in resting on the rail of a fence or upon the horn of a cow. Also they marvelled at its stupidity when attacked with sticks or stones, — as often flying toward the danger as away from it. But they sympathized with its struggles in the spider's net, and rejoiced to see it burst through the meshes. The following examples, selected from hundreds of compositions, will serve to suggest the wide range of these curious studies : —

DRAGON-FLIES AND SUNSHINE

Tombō ya,
Hi no sasu kataë
Taté-yuku!

O dragon-fly! ever towards the sun you rise and soar!

Hiatari no
Doté ya hinémosu
Tombō tobu.

Over the sunlit bank, all day long, the dragon-flies flit to and fro.

Go-roku shaku
Onoga kumoi no
Tombō kana !

Poor dragon-fly ! — the [blue] space of five or six feet
[above him] he thinks to be his own sky !

Tombō no
Muki wo soroëru
Nishi-hi kana !

Ah, the sunset-glow ! Now all the dragon-flies are
shooting in the same direction.

Tombō ya !
Sora é hanarété
Kurékakari.

Dusk approaches: see! the dragon-flies have risen
toward the sky !

Hoshi hitotsu
Miru madé asobu
Tombō kana!

O dragon-fly ! you continue to sport until the first star
appears !

FLIGHT OF DRAGON-FLIES

Tō yama ya,
Tombō tsui-yuki,
Tsui-kaëru.

Quickly the dragon-fly starts for the distant mountain, but as quickly returns.

Yukiōté,
Dochiramo soréru
Tombō kana !

Meeting in flight, how wonderfully do tne dragon-flies glance away from each other !

Narabu ka to
Miété wa soréru
Tombō kana !

Lo ! the dragon-flies that seemed to fly in line all scatter away from each other.

MENTIONED IN LOVE-SONGS

Kagérō no
Kagé tomo waré wa
Nari ni kéri
Aruka nakika no
Kimi ga nasaké ni.

Even as the shadow of a dragon-fly [1] I have become, by reason of the slightness of your love.

Obotsu kana !
Yumé ka ? utsusu ka ?
Kagerō no
Honoméku yori mo
Hakanakarishi wa !

O my doubt ! Is it a dream or a reality ? — more fugitive than even the dim flitting of a dragon-fly ! [2]

Tombō ya !
Mi wo mo kogasazu,
Naki mo sézu !

Happy dragon-fly ! — never self-consumed by longing, — never even uttering a cry !

STRANGENESS AND BEAUTY

Tombō no
Kao wa ōkata
Médama kana !

O the face of the dragon-fly ! — almost nothing but eyes !

---

[1] The word *kagérō* here means " dragon-fly." There is another word *kagérō* meaning " gossamer." Though written alike in Romaji, these two terms are represented in Japanese by very different characters.

[2] The thought suggested is, — " Can it be true that we were ever united, even for a moment ? "

Koë naki wo,
Tombō munen ni
Miyuru kana!

O dragon-fly! you appear to be always angry because
you have no voice!

Sémi ni makénu
Hagoromo mochishi,
Tombō kana!

O dragon-fly! the celestial raiment [1] you possess is nowise inferior to that of the cicada!

LIGHTNESS OF DRAGON-FLIES

Tsubamé yori
Tombō wa mono mo
Ugokasazu.

More lightly even than the swallow does the dragon-fly
touch things without moving them.

Tombō ya,
Tori no fumarénu
Éda no saki!

---

[1] Literally " feather-robe " (*hagoromo*); — this is the name given
to the raiment supposed to be worn by the " Sky-People " — angelic
inhabitants of the Buddhist heaven. The *hagoromo* enables its
wearer to soar through space; and the poet compares the wings of the
beautiful insect to such a fairy robe.

Dragon-flies

O dragon-fly, you perch on the tip of the spray where never a bird can tread !

STUPIDITY OF DRAGON-FLIES

Utsu-tsuĕ no
Saki ni tomarishi,
Tombō kana !

O dragon-fly ! you light upon the end of the very stick with which one tries to strike you down !

Tachi-kaëru
Tombō tomaru
Tsubuté kana !

See ! the dragon-fly returns to perch upon the pebble that was thrown at it !

DRAGON-FLIES AND SPIDERS

Kumonosu no
Atari ni asobu
Tombō kana !

Ah ! the poor dragon-fly, sporting beside the spider's web !

Sasagami no
Ami no hazurété,
Tombō kana!

Good dragon-fly! — he has extricated himself from the
net of the spider!

Kumo gaki mo
Yaburu kihoi ya,
Oni-tombō!

Through even the spider's fence he has force to burst
his way! — O the demon-dragon-fly!

HEEDLESS OF FLOWERS

Tombō ya!
Hana-no ni mo mé wa
Hosorasézu.

Ah, the dragon-fly! even in the flower-field he never
half-shuts his eyes![1]

Tombō ya!
Hana ni wa yoradé,
Ishi no ué.

O the dragon-fly! — heedless of the flowers, he lights
upon a stone!

---

[1] Alluding to the fact that one half-closes one's eyes, — in order to
shadow them, and so to see more distinctly, — when looking at some
beautiful object. — Perhaps the rendering, "never makes his eyes
narrower," would better express the exact sense of the original.

Tombō ya !
Hana naki kui ni
Sumi-narai.

Ah, the dragon-fly ! content to dwell upon a flowerless stake !

Néta ushi no
Tsuno ni hararénu,
Yamma kana !

O great dragon-fly ! will you never leave the horn of the sleeping ox ?

Kui no saki
Nanika ajiwō
Tombō kana ?

O dragon-fly ! what can you be tasting on the top of that fence-stake ?

Of course these compositions make but slight appeal to æsthetic sentiment : they are merely curious, for the most part. But they help us to understand something of the soul of the elder Japan. The people who could find delight, century after century, in watching the ways of insects, and in making such verses about them, must have comprehended, better than we, the simple pleasure of existence. They could not, indeed, describe the magic of nature as our great Western poets have done; but they could feel the beauty of the world without its sorrow, and rejoice in that beauty, much after the manner of inquisitive and happy children.

If they could have seen the dragon-fly as we can see it, — if they could have looked at that elfish head with its jewelled ocelli, its marvellous compound eyes, its astonishing mouth, under the microscope, — how much more extraordinary would the creature have seemed to them! . . . And yet, though wise enough to have lost that fresh naïve pleasure in natural observation which colors the work of these quaint poets, we are not so very much wiser than they were in regard to the real wonder of the insect. We are able only to estimate more accurately the immensity of our ignorance concerning it. Can we ever hope for a Natural History with colored plates that will show us how the world appears to the faceted eyes of a dragon-fly?

V

CATCHING dragon-flies has been for hundreds of years a favorite amusement of Japanese children.

It begins with the hot season, and lasts during the greater part of the autumn. There are many old poems about it, — describing the recklessness of the little hunters. To-day, just as in other centuries, the excitement of the chase leads them into all sorts of trouble: they tumble down embankments, and fall into ditches, and scratch and dirty themselves most fearfully, — heedless of thorns or mud-holes or quagmires, — heedless of heat, — heedless even of the dinner-hour: —

> Méshi-doki mo
> Modori wasurété,
> Tombō-tsuri!

Even at the hour of the noon-day meal they forget to return home, — the children catching dragon-flies !

> Hadaka-go no
> Tombō tsuri-kéri
> Hiru no tsuji !

The naked child has been catching dragon-flies at the road-crossing, — heedless of the noon-sun !

But the most celebrated poem in relation to this amusement is of a touching character. It was

written by the famous female poet, Chiyo of
Kaga, after the death of her little boy: —

> Tombō-tsuri! —
> Kyō wa doko madé
> Itta yara!

"Catching dragon-flies! . . . I wonder where *he* has
gone to-day!"

The verse is intended to suggest, not to express,
the emotion of the mother. She sees children
running after dragon-flies, and thinks of her own
dead boy who used to join in the sport, — and
so finds herself wondering, in presence of the
infinite Mystery, what has become of the little
soul. Whither has it gone? — in what shadowy
play does it now find delight?

Dragon-flies are captured sometimes with nets,
sometimes by means of bamboo rods smeared
at the end with birdlime, sometimes even by
striking them down with a light stick or switch.
The use of a switch, however, is not commonly
approved; for the insect is thereby maimed, and
to injure it unnecessarily is thought to be unlucky,
— by reason, perhaps, of its supposed relation to

the dead. A very successful method of dragon-fly-catching — practised chiefly in the Western provinces — is to use a captured female dragon-fly as a decoy. One end of a long thread is fastened to the insect's tail, and the other end of the thread to a flexible rod. By moving the rod in a particular way the female can be kept circling on her wings at the full length of the thread; and a male is soon attracted. As soon as he clings to the female, a slight jerk of the rod will bring both insects into the angler's hand. With a single female for lure, it is easy to capture eight or ten males in succession.

During these dragon-fly hunts the children usually sing little songs, inviting the insect to approach. There are many such dragon-fly songs; and they differ according to province. An Izumo song of this class [1] contains a curious allusion to the traditional conquest of Korea in the third century by the armies of the Empress Jingō; the male dragon-fly being thus addressed: —
" Thou, the male, King of Korea, art not ashamed to flee from the Queen of the East ? "

---

[1] Cited in *Glimpses of Unfamiliar Japan;* vol. II., p. 372.

In Tōkyō to-day the little dragon-fly hunters usually sing the following:—

> Tombō! tombō!
> O-tomari!—
> Ashita no ichi ni,
> Shiōkara kōté,
> Néburashō!

Dragon-fly! dragon-fly! honorably wait!— to-morrow at the market I will buy some *shiōkara* and let you lick it!

Children also find amusement in catching the larva of the dragon-fly. This larva has many popular names; but is usually called in Tōkyō *taiko-mushi*, or "drum-insect," because it moves its forelegs in the water somewhat as a man moves his arms while playing upon a drum.

A most extraordinary device for catching dragon-flies is used by the children of the province of Kii. They get a long hair,— a woman's hair,— and attach a very small pebble to each end of it, so as to form a miniature "bolas"; and this they sling high into the air. A dragon-fly pounces upon the passing object; but the moment that he seizes it, the hair twists round his body, and the weight of the pebbles brings him to the ground. I wonder whether this method of bolassing dragon-flies is known anywhere outside of Japan.

Buddhist Names of Plants and Animals

AT one time I hoped to compile a glossary of the Buddhist names given to Japanese animals and plants; and I began to collect material for the work. But I then knew very little about the real difficulties of such an undertaking. To mention only one, I may observe that in almost every province of Japan the folk-speech is different; and the difference appears even in the names given to certain plants, insects, reptiles, fishes, and birds. Such names must be learned, of course, from the lips of peasants and of fishermen; and that which I wished to do could never be well done except through the patient labors of a folklore society. And now I find that, instead of being able to prepare the glossary intended, I must content myself with a few general notes upon the subject.

But perhaps these notes — relics of an undertaking for which I possessed neither the requisite scholarship nor the means — will have at least a suggestive worth to future explorers in this unfamiliar region of Far-Eastern folklore.

*
* *

The name Buddha appears in the appellations of several trees and plants. *Marubushukan,* or " Round-Fingers-of-Buddha," is the name of a kind of lemon-tree, — so called from the very remarkable shape of its fruit. The Chinese hibiscus is called *Bussōgé,* or " Buddha's mulberry "; and a variety of rock-moss is popularly known by the picturesque names of *Hotoké-no-tsumé* and *Bukkōsō,* — both signifying " Finger-nails of Buddha." A kind of yam is called *Tsukuné-imo,* — which appellation, as written with the proper Chinese characters, signifies " Buddha's-hand potato "; and a variety of clover is honored by the name *Hotoké-no-za,* or " Buddha's-throne."

Names of Bodhisattvas and of other Buddhist divinities are also to be found in the appellations of plants and animals. The name of Kwannon (Âvalokitesvara) appears in the term *Kwannon-*

chiku, or "Bamboo of Kwannon"; and several different plants are known, in different provinces, by the name *Kwannon-sō,* or "Herb of Kwannon." The name of Fugen (Samantabhadra) has been given to a variety of cherry-tree, — the *Fugen-zakura,* or "Fugen's cherry-tree." The name of Dai-Mokukenren (Mahamaudgalyâyana), — shortened by popular usage into Mokuren, — figures both in the common appellation of the *Ficus pumila,* known as *Mokuren,* and in that of the *Magnolia conspicuà,* usually called *Haku-mokuren,* or "White-Mokuren." The name of Brahma, — known to Japanese Buddhism as Bonten, — appears in the designation of a kind of upland rice, *Bonten-mai.* The memory of Bō-dai-Daruma (Bôdhidharma) is preserved in the popular appellation of the *Aster spatufolium,* called *Daruma-gihu,* or "Daruma's chrysanthemum," — as well as in the name of the swamp-cabbage, *Daruma-sō,* or "Daruma's plant." Two fishes also have been named after this patriarch: the *Priacanthus Niphonius,* which is called *Daruma-dai,* or "Daruma's sea-bream"; and the *Synanceia erosa,* popularly known as *Daruma-kasago,* — "kasago" being properly the name of the fish scientifically called *sebastes inermis.*

More curious than any of the above terms, however, is the popular name for a species of grain-weevil, *Kokuzō*, — "Kokuzō" being the Japanese appellation of the great Bodhisattva Âkâsapratishthita.

The term Bosatsu (Bodhisattva) also appears in some plant-names. A variéty of rose is known as the *Bosatsu-ibara,* or "Thorny-Rose of the Bodhisattva"; and a kind of rice is called *Bosatsu.*

The term Rakan (Arhat) forms a prefix to several plant-names. *Rakan-baku,* or "Arhat's oak," is the popular name of the *Thuya dolobrata*. *Rakan-shō,* or "Arhat's Pine," is the common appellation of the *Podocarpus macrophylla;* and the name *Rakan-maki,* or "Arhat's *maki*" ("maki" being the Japanese name for the *podocarpus chinensis*) — has been given to the umbrella-pine. And the fruit of a tree, of which I cannot find the scientific name, is called in several provinces *Rakan,* or "the Arhat," because it curiously resembles in shape the rude stone images of Arhats set up in temple-gardens.

Kukai, or Kōbōdaishi, the great Japanese patriarch of the Shingon sect, also has a place in this nomenclature. *Kōbō-mugi,* or "Wheat of Kōbō-daishi," is a common name for the *Carex macrocephala ;* and a variety of chestnut is called *Kōbōdaishi - kawazu -no-kuri,* — "The Chestnut that Kōbōdaishi did not eat."

Many names of plants or living creatures refer to Buddhist customs, legends, rites, or beliefs. The word *bōzu,* "priest " — (the origin of our word " bonze ") — has been attached to several plant-names. No less than three different herbs are known, in different parts of the country, by the name of *Bōzugusa,* or " Priest-grass." In the dialect of Chikuzen a kind of turtle is called *Umi-bōzu,* or " Priest of the Sea," — a name, by the way, also given to a mythical marine-monster, often represented in Japanese picture-books. The name of the famous Bo-tree of Buddhist tradition has been given in Japan, not only to the *Ficus religiosa,* but also to the *Tilia miqueliana,* popularly called *Bōdaijū* (Bodhidruma). The great Buddhist festival of the spring-equinox, the festival of the Higan, or " Further Shore," has furnished names for two plants which blossom about that time, — the *Higan-zakura* or " Higan cherry-tree " (*Prunus*

miqueliana), and the *Higan-bana,* or "Flower
of Higan" (*Lycoris radiata*). What we term
"Job's Tears" are in Japan called *Zuẓudama,*
or Buddhist rosary-beads; and a kind of dove
is known — probably because of its markings
— as the *Zuẓukaké-bato,* or "Rosary-bearing
Dove." The *Allium victoriale* is called *Gyoja-
ninniku,* or "Hermit's garlic" ("gyōja" being
the Buddhist term for hermit); and the popular Japanese name for the Bleeding-heart is
Keman-sō, or "*Keman*-herb," — an appellation
probably due to the resemblance of the flower
to the *Keman,* or decoration, placed upon the
head of the statue of Buddha. Perhaps the
water-arum has the most curious of all such
Buddhist appellations: its Japanese name, *Koku-
ẓen-sō* literally signifies the "Small-sitting-in-
Dhyâna-meditation-plant."

The word *Sennin,* — commonly translated as
"Genius" or "Fairy," but originally meaning
Rishi, — a being who has acquired supernatural
power and unlimited life by force of ascetic
practices, — occasionally appears in plant-names.
A variety of Clematis is known as *Sennin-sō,*
or "Fairy-weed"; and a kind of cactus has

received the grotesque appellation of *Sennin-shō,* or "Sennin's-Palm," — the palm of the hand being referred to.

The Sanscrit term Yaksha, signifying a man-devouring demon, appears in several plant-names under its Japanese form, — *Yasha.* The cone of the *Aldus firma* is picturesquely called *Yasha-bushi,* or "Yaksha's-joint"; and a water-plant is known by the curious name of *Yasha-bishaku,* or "Yaksha's Ladle."

Very many Japanese names of vegetables, birds, fishes, and insects, have attached to them as a prefix the word *Oni,* a Buddhist term for "demon" or "devil," — just as in English folk-speech we have such names for plants and insects as "Devil's-apron, " "Devil-wood," "Devil's-fingers," "Devil's-horse," and "Devil's-darning-needle." The tiger-lily is known in Japan by the equally fantastic name of *Oni-yuri,* or "Devil-lily." A species of coix is called *Oni-zuzudama,* or "Devil's rosary-beads." The bur-marigold is called *Oni-bari,* or "Devil's needle"; and a water-weed, injurious to lotos-cultivation, is popularly termed the *Oni-basu,* or "Demon-lotos." This prefix of *Oni* is probably attached to hundreds of folk-names of flora and fauna: I have myself collected no less than seventy-one examples. Nevertheless, few of them are interesting.

The word *Kijin,* or *Kishin,* signifying a kind of goblin recognized by Japanese Buddhism, is similarly used as a prefix;—for example, a sort of needle-grass is known as *Kishin-sō,* or "Goblin-weed." *Kijo,* another Buddhist word signifying a kind of female goblin, appears in the common name of an orchid,—*Kijoran,* or "Goblin-orchid." Also there is a prefix, *Ki,*—abbreviation of a term for demon or goblin,—which sometimes figures in plant-names: the *Pardanthus chinensis,* for instance, is called in Japan *Kisen,* meaning "Goblin-fan." It is worthy of remark that these devilish names are given to vegetables or to animals, not merely because of some ugly or extraordinary shape, but even because of remarkable size. Thus a species of lark is called *Oni-hibari,* or "Demon-lark," because it happens to be a much larger bird than the common field-lark; and a very large kind of dragon-fly is designated for the same reason *Oni-yamma,* or "Demon-dragonfly."

Many Buddhist names, both of creatures and of plants, are ghostly. A pretty green grass-hopper is called *Hotoké-uma,* or "the Buddha-horse"; — the head of the insect curiously resembling the head of a horse in shape. But the word *hotoké* also means the spirit of a dead person, — all good persons being supposed by popular faith to become Buddhas; — and the real meaning of the name *Hotoké-uma* is "The Horse of the Dead." Now during the great three-days' Festival of the Dead in the seventh month, it is believed that many spirits revisit their homes, or their former friends, either with the help of insects or actually in the form of insects. The name of this grasshopper really implies that it is used as a horse by the shadowy visitors. . . . Again, we find the word *shōryō,* — a general term for the spirits of ancestors worshipped according to Buddhist rite, — coupled with the name of a dragon-fly: *Shōryō-yamma,* "the Dragon-fly of the Ancestral Spirits." *Shōrai-tombō,* or "Ghost Dragon-fly," and *Ki-yamma,* a term of similar meaning, are names likewise intended to suggest the relation of the insect to the invisible world. Equally weird is the name by which the mole-cricket is known in the dialect of Kyōto, — a name probably suggested by the creature's underground life, — *Shōrai-mushi,* or " Ghost-insect." Among appellations of plants one finds also such terms as *Yurei-daké,* or " Ghost-bamboo," and *Yurei-bana,* or " Ghost-flower," — the latter name being not inappropriately given to a species of delicate mushroom.

Some of the Buddhist names, although highly interesting in themselves, could not be understood by the Western reader without the help of pictorial illustration, because they have reference to the furniture of temples, or to particular articles used in Buddhist religio s service. Such, for example, is the name of a tree popularly known as *Sankō-matsu,* or " Sankō-pine " ; — the term " Sankō " (Sanscrit, *Vadjra*) signifying a brass object, — shaped much like the classic representation of a thunderbolt, with prongs at either end, — which priests use in certain rites as a symbol of supernatural power. Such also is the name *Hossugai,* or " *Hossu*-shell," given to the beautiful glass-sponge, *Hyalonema Sieboldii,* because of its resemblance to the " hossu," — a brush or duster of long white hair used in Buddhist religious service. And such, again, is the excellent name of a little insect called the *Koromo-sémi,* or "Priest's-robe cicada," because the general form and color of the creature, when resting with closed wings, really suggest the figure of a priest in his "koromo." But unless you had seen the insect, and the kind of "koromo" thus referred to, you could not appreciate the graphic worth of the appellation.

Very remarkable Buddhist names have been given to some species of birds. There is a bird, known to ornithologists as *Eurystomus orientalis,* which is called *Buppōsō,* because its cry resembles the sound of the word *Buppōsō.* This word is a Japanese equivalent for the Sanscrit term *Triratna* or *Ratnatraya,* — "Three Jewels"; — the syllable *Bu* standing for *Butsu,* "the Buddha"; *pō,* for *hō,* "the Law"; and *sō,* for "the Priesthood." The bird is also called *Sambōchō,* or "the *Sambō*-bird"; — the word "Sambō" being a literal translation of *Triratna.* Another bird, of which I do not know the scientific appellation, is called the *Jihishinchō,* or "Compassionate-Mind-Bird," — because its call resembles the utterance of the phrase *Jihi-shin,* "Compassionate Mind," which forms one of the epithets of

the Buddha. " This bird," my informant writes,
lives only in the neighborhood of Nikkō, where
in the summer it may be heard continually crying
out, ' O thou Compassionate Mind ! — O thou
Compassionate Mind ! ' " . . . Almost equally
interesting is the common Buddhist name for the
hototogisu (*Cuculus poliocephalus*), a species of
cuckoo much celebrated by Japanese poets. It is
called *Mujō-dori,* or " the Bird of Impermanency." This name would not appear to be
derived from the bird's note, which is popularly
interpreted as " *Honzon kakétaka ?* " — meaning,
" Has the *honzon* yet been suspended ? " (The
" honzon " is the sacred picture displayed in
temples upon the eighth day of the fourth month,
— a little before the time at which the bird makes
its annual appearance.) It seems to me more
probable that the name was given in the signification, " Bird of Death " ; — for the word *mujō* has
also the meaning of death as change ; and this
meaning is strongly suggested by the strange fact
that the *hototogisu* is supposed to come from the
spirit-world. It is also called *Tama-mukaē-dori,*
or the " Ghost-welcoming Bird," because it is
said to meet and to greet the spirits of the dead
on their journey over the Mountain of Shidé to

the River of Souls. There are many ghostly legends and fancies about the *hototogisu*; and this weird folklore sufficiently explains why the bird is known in the provinces by no less than fifty-two different names!

The *uguisu*, a variety of nightingale, and the sweetest-voiced of all Japanese singers, does not appear to have any popular Buddhist name; but its flute-like call is said to be an utterance of the word *Hokkekyō*, which is the popular name for the Saddharma-Pundarîka-Sûtra, — the grand scripture of the Nichiren or Hokké sect. And Buddhist piety asserts that the bird passes its life in chanting the praise of the Sûtra of the Lotos of the Good Law. So that the *uguisu* is really regarded as a Buddhist bird. Another bird which seems to have some relation to Buddhism is the snowy heron, to which the extraordinary appellation of *Bonnō-sagi*, or " *Bonnō*-heron," has been given. "Bonnō" is a Buddhist term for worldly desire, lust, passion; and I am not able to say why it appears in the name of the bird.

The difficulty of guessing at the origin of these Buddhist names cannot even be imagined without the help of examples. The literal meaning, in

many cases, serves only to mislead investigation.
For instance, the hammer-headed shark is known
on parts of the Kyūshū coast by the extraordinary appellation, *Nembutsu-bō,* or " *Nembutsu-*
Priest." The word *Nembutsu* is the name of the
invocation, "Namu Amida Butsu!" — (Salutation to the Buddha Amitâbha!) — uttered by the
pious of many sects as a prayer, and *especially as
a prayer for the dead.* The grim suggestiveness
of the name *Nembutsu-bō* reminded me that the
modern French word for shark is, according to
Littré, only a corruption of "Requiem," — the
appellation originally implying (as stated by Père
Dutertre in 1667) that for the man caught by
a shark there was nothing to be done except to
chant his requiem. But I was wrong in imagin-
ing that the Buddhist name *Nembutsu-bō* implied
something of the same kind. The real meaning
of the term is proved by another Buddhist name
for the same monster, — *Shumoku-zamé,* or
" *Shumoku-*shark." The word " Shumoku "
signifies a peculiar " T "-shaped mallet with
which the priest strikes a gong during the repetition of the *Nembutsu* and of other prayers.
(I may observe that the same kind of mallet is
used to sound a gong during the chanting of the

Nembutsu, in some pious households, before the family shrine.) It was this use of the mallet and gong, during the repetition of the invocation, that suggested the term *Nembutsu-bō* as an alternate name for the *Shumoku-zamé,* or " Mallet-shark ; " — and the true signification of *Nembutsu-bō* is not " The *Nembutsu*-Priest," but " The Priest with the Mallet."

Songs of Japanese Children

❦

UNDER the influence of twenty-seven thousand public schools the old folk-literature of Japan, the unwritten literature of song and tradition, is rapidly passing out of memory. Even within my own recollection one variety of this oral literature, partly corresponding to our own literature of the nursery, has been greatly affected by the new order of things. When I first came to Japan the children were singing the old songs which they had been taught by their grandfathers and grandmothers, — the home-teaching being usually left to the grandparents. But to-day the little folk, at play in the streets or in the temple-courts, are singing new songs learned in the class-room, — songs set to music written according to the Western scale; — and the far more interesting pre-Meiji songs are now but seldom heard.

135

As yet, however, they are not entirely forgotten, — partly because many of them are in-
separably connected with games that cannot be
suddenly superseded, — partly because there are
still alive some millions of delightful grandfathers
and grandmothers who never studied under
organ-playing schoolmasters, and who like to
hear the children repeat the ditties of long ago.
But I suppose that after these charming old people have been gathered to their ancestors, most of
the songs which they taught will cease to be sung.
Happily the Japanese folklorists have been exert-
ing themselves to preserve such unwritten literature ; and their labors have enabled me to attempt
the present paper.

Out of a great number of the old-time child-
songs and nonsense-verses, carefully copied and
translated for me, I have endeavored to make a
fairly representative selection, — grouping all the
examples under six subject-titles, in the following
order : —

I. — Songs of Weather and Sky.

II. — Songs about Animals.

III. — Miscellaneous Play-Songs.

IV. — Narrative Songs.

V. — Battledoor and Ball Songs.

VI. — Lullabies.

The classification is very loose, especially as regards the third group; but I think that it is justified by the strangely indefinite character of many compositions.

Of course the plain English renderings can give an idea of the Japanese verses only as flowers pressed and dried between the leaves of a book can represent the living blossoms in their natural environment. The queer rhythm of the rhymeless lines, the naïveté of the Japanese words, the curious little airs, — difficult to memorize as bird-warblings, — and the sweet freshness of many child-voices chanting in unison : these help to make the true charm of the original song, and all are equally irreproducible.

A good deal of the exotic may be discovered in these cullings ; but the reader will occasionally find something to remind him of familiar nursery-rhymes. Children, all the world over, think and feel in nearly the same way on certain subjects, and sing of like experiences. In almost every country they sing about the sun and the moon, — about wind and rain, — about birds and beasts, — about flowers and trees and brooks ; — also about such daily household duties as drawing water, making fire, cooking and washing. Yet I believe that, even within these limits, the differences between Japanese child-literature and other child-literature will be found more interesting than the resemblances.

I

SONGS OF WEATHER AND SKY

(Tōkyō Sunset-song.)

Yu-yaké !
Ko-yaké !
Ashita wa tenki ni naré.

Evening-burning !
Little burning !
Weather, be fair to-morrow.! [1]

(Kite-flying song — Province of Iga.)

Tengu San,
Kazé okuré !
Kazé ga nakéra
Zéni okuré !

---

[1] This little song is still sung by the children in my neighborhood whenever a beautiful sunset occurs.

Tengu San [*Lord Mountain-Spirit*],
Please to give me some wind!
If there be no wind,
Please give some money![1]

(*Rain-song — Province of Tosa.*)

Amé, amé, furi-yamé!
O-tera no maë no
Kaki no ki no moto dé
Kiji no ko ga nakuzo!

Rain, rain! stop falling! — At the foot of the *kaki*-tree
in front of the temple, the young of the pheasant is crying!

(*Snow-song — Province of Iga.*)

Yuki wa chira-chira!
Kumo wa hai-daraké!

Snow is fluttering, — *chira-chira!*
The clouds are full of ashes![2]

---

[1] In Tōkyō the little kite-flyers usually sing, —
> Kazé no kami wa
> Yowai na!

("Ah! the God of the Wind is weak to-day!")   In Izumo they sing, —
> Daisen no yama kara
> O-Kazé fuété!
> Koi yo!

("Come, August-Wind, and blow from the mountain Daisen!")
[2] White ashes of wood are referred to.

(Province of Izumo.)

Yuki ya !
Konko ya !
Araré ya !
Konko ya !
Omaë no sédo dé
Dango mo niéru,
Azuki mo niéru,
Yamado wa modoru,
Akago wa hoëru,
Shakushi wa miézu,
Yaré isogashiya nā !

Snow-grains! hail-grains ! — In your kitchen dumplings are boiling; beans too are boiling; the huntsman is returning; the baby is squalling; the ladle is missing ! — O what a flurry and worry !

(Star-song — Province of Iga.)

— Hoshi San, Hoshi San !
Hitori-boshi dé dénu monja ;
Sen mo, man mo déru monja.

— Mr. Star, Mr. Star !
For a single star to rise alone is not right ;
Even a thousand, even ten thousand should rise together ! [1]

---

[1] Sung when the first stars begin to twinkle after sundown.

(Moon-song — Province of Shinano.)

> O-Tsuki Sama,
> Kwannon-dō orité,
> Mamma agaré!
> — Mamma wa iya-iya:
> Ammo nara mitsu kuryō!

— O Lady Moon,
Come down from over the Temple of Kwannon,
And help yourself to some boiled rice!
— Rice? no! I do not like rice.
But if you have *ammochi*,[1] let me have three!

(Province of Kii.)

> — O-Tsuki Sama, ikutsu?
> — Jiu-san hitotsu.
> — Sorya mada wakai:
> Waka-buné é notté,
> Kara madé wataré

— Lady Moon, how old are you?
— Thirteen and one.
— That is still young:
In the Ship of Youth embarking,
Cross over the sea to China!

---

[1] Rice-cakes stuffed with a mixture of sugar and bean-flour.

(Province of Tosa.)

— O-Tsuki Sama
Momo-iro !
— Daré ga iuta ?
— Ama ga iuta.
— Ama no kuchi wo
Hikisaké !

— O Lady Moon, your face is the color of a peach ! —
Who said so ? — A nun said so. — Pinch and tear the mouth
of that nun !

(Province of Suwŏ.)

O-Tsuki Sama,
O-Tsuki Sama,
Mōshi ! mōshi ! —
Néko to nézumi ga,
Isshō-daru sagété,
Fuji-no-yama wo
Ima koëta !

O Lady Moon !
O Lady Moon !
I say ! I say !
A cat and a rat,
Carrying a one-shō barrel [of saké],
The Mountain of Fuji
Just now crossed over ![1]

[1] Sung when a cloud passes over the Moon. The cat and the rat
are playful goblins, of course, — such as figure in children's picture-

II

SONGS ABOUT ANIMALS[1]

OF child-songs about insects and reptiles, birds and beasts, the number is surprising, — almost every Japanese village having one or two songs of its own belonging to this class. The great majority are brief compositions of from two to eight lines. Some of the better ones recall English nursery-rhymes on kindred topics, — such nursery-rhymes, for example, as, " Bat, bat, come under my hat ! " — " Lady-bird, lady-bird, fly away home ! " — " Cuckoo, cuckoo, what do you do ? " — " A pie sat on a pear-tree," etc., etc. Very probably several of the following selections are older than most of our nursery-rhymes. Variants of nearly all exist in multitude.

---

[1] See also, for a small collection of Izumo songs relating to natural history, the chapter " In a Japanese Garden," in my *Glimpses of Unfamiliar Japan*.

---

books. The purpose of the song is to make the Moon peep out again.

An Izumo moon-song, more interesting than any of these, will be found in my *Kokoro*, pp. 75-76.

(Dove-song — Tōkyō.)

Hato
Poppō!
Mamé ga tabétai.[1]

"*Poppō*," says the dove, — "I want to eat some beans."

(Crow-song — Tōkyō.)

Karasu!
Karasu!
Kanzaburō!
Oya no on wo wasuréna yo!

O crow! O crow! Kanzaburō![2] — never forget the goodness of your parents!

(Owl-song — Tōkyō.)

Gorosuké-hōkō
Muda-bōkō!

Gorosuké's service, useless service!

---

[1] Or *kuttai.*

[2] Kanzaburō is a very common form of masculine proper name, — here probably given to the bird merely for the sake of the sound. — The song was no doubt suggested by the old proverb, *Karasu ni hampo no kō ari*: "The filial duty of feeding one's parents is known even to the crow." It is said that the old crows, unable to forage for themselves, are fed by their offspring. — Children sing this song when they see the crows flying home at sundown.

(Bird-song — Province of Isé.)

Suzumé wa, Chū-Chū-Chūzaburō!
Karasu wa, Ka-Ka-Kanzaburō!
Tombi wa, Toyama no kanétataki!
    Ichi nichi tataité ; —
        Komé isshō!
        Awa isshō!

As for the sparrow, — Chū-Chū-Chūzaburō,
As for the crow, — Ka-Ka-Kanzaburō;
As for the kite,[1] — the Bell-ringer of Toyama :
    All day he taps his bell,
    [*Crying*] Rice, one *shō!*[2]
        Millet, one *shō!*

The personal names Kanzaburō, Chūzaburō,
and Gorosuké, are common names of men. No
doubt that the sparrow's sharp cry, resembling the
sound *chū,* first suggested the use of the name
Chūzaburō in the foregoing nursery-rhyme; and
the crow was probably called Kanzaburō because
its caw sounds like the syllable *Ka.*[1] But there

---

[1] Another version reads, " Tobi wa, Tō-Tō-Tōzaburō." Tōzaburō,
like Chūzaburō and Kanzaburō, is a real name.

[2] One *shō* is equal to about a quart and a half.

---

[1] I may observe also that the crow is popularly said to
cry, *Kawa! kawa!* (" River! river!"), — meaning, " Let
us go to the river!" The sound of the cawing really resembles the sound of the word *Kawa.*

is a curious legend about the name given to the owl, — Gorosuké. A long time ago, in the house of some great samurai, there was a retainer called Gorosuké. This Gorosuké was naturally dull; and the very first time that a duty of importance was confided to him, he made such a blunder that serious mischief resulted. Therefore everybody laughed at him, and put him to shame; and at last he killed himself. Then his spirit took the form of the little owl which now bears his name; and all night long this owl cries out, in a tone of utter despair, —

> "Gorosuké's service !
> Useless service !"

(Hare-song — Tōkyō.)

> "Usagi, usagi,
> Nani wo mité hanéru ? "
> "Jiu-go-ya no O-Tsuki Sama
> Mité hanéru !
> *Hyoi !*
> *Hyoi !* "

—"Hare, hare! what do you see that makes you jump?" — "Seeing the Lady-Moon of the fifteenth night, I jump! — *Hyoi! byoi!*"[1]

---

[1] At the words "hyoi! hyoi!" all the singers jump together.

(Sparrow-song — Tōkyō.)

Suzumé no atsumari :
Chi-ĭ, chi-ĭ — pappa!
Daré ni atattémo
Okoruna yo!
Okorunara hajimé kara
Yoran ga yoi.

Hear the gathering of the sparrows! — *chi-ĭ, chi-ĭ,* — *pappa!*[1] — Be not so angry with everybody who happens to touch you! Better in the beginning not to have come at all, than to get angry thus!

(Song about the white heron — Province of Isé.)

Shirosagi, shirosagi,
Nazé kubi ga nagai ?
— Hidaruté nagai.
— Hidarukya ta uté.
— Ta ucha, doro ga tsuku.
— Doro ga tsukya, haraë.
— Haraya, itai.

— White-heron, white-heron! why is your neck so long ? — Because of hunger it became long. — If you are hungry, go and till the rice-field. — I should get muddy if I were to till the rice-field. — If you get muddy, you can

---

[1] *Chi-ĭ* is an onomatope invented to describe the angry chirping of the sparrow; *pappa* signifies the sound of the quick flapping of its wings.

brush the mud off. — If I should brush myself, it would
hurt me !

(Toad-song — Province of Tosa.)

Hiki-San, Hiki San, dété gonsé
Denya mogusa suéru-zo !

Toad, toad, come out of your hole !   If you don't come
out I shall give you a moxa !

(Kite-song — Province of Izumo.)

Tobi ! tobi ! mauté misé !
Ashita no ban ni,
Karasu ni kakushité,
Nezúmi yaru !

Kite ! kite ! let me see you dance !   To-morrow evening, without letting the crows see it, I shall give you a rat !

(Bat-song — Province of Izumo.)

Komori, koi ! saké nomashō !
Saké ga nakya, taru furashō.

Bat, come hither, and you will drink some *saké!* If
there be no *saké* [ready], I will pour out some from the
barrel.

(Firefly-song — Province of Izumo.)

Hotaru koi midzu nomashō :
Achi no midzu wa nigai zo ;

Kochi no midzu wa amai zo;
Amai hō é tondé koi!

Firefly, come hither, and you shall have water to drink! Yonder the water is bitter; — here the water is sweet! Come, fly this way, to the sweet side!

(Firefly-song — Province of Isé.)

Hotaru, koi!
Tsuchi-mushi, koi!
Onoga hikari dé
Jō mottékoi!

Firefly, come hither!
Earth-insect,[1] come!
By your own light
Bring me a letter!

(Tōkyō.)

O-wata, koi! koi!
Mamé kuwashō!
O-mamma ga iyanara,
Toto kuwashō!

Come here, *o-wata!*[2] come here! I will give you beans to eat. If there be no boiled rice, then I will give you some fish.

---

[1] *Tsuchi-mushi,* literally, is "earth-insect" or "earth-worm"; but in this little song it probably means "glow-worm."

[2] The name "o-wata" (*honorable cotton*) is given to a small purplish fly having a fluffy white protuberance on its tail, resembling a tuft of cotton.

(Butterfly-song.)

Chōchō! chōchō!
Na no ha ni tomaré!
Na no ha ga iyénara,
Té ni tomaré!

Butterfly! butterfly! light upon the '*na*-leaf!¹ If you do not like the *na*-leaf, perch upon my hand!

(Tōkyō Song.)

Chōchō, tombō mo,
Tori no uchi,
Yama saëzuru no wa,
Matsumushi,
Suzumushi,
Kutsuwamushi,
Ō-chōko choï no choï!

The butterfly, and the dragon-fly, too, at the house of the bird. Oh, the twittering in the mountains! The Pine-Insect, the Bell-Insect, the Bridle-bit-Insect all together, — *Ō-chōko choï no choï!*

(Sung by children chasing dragon-flies.)

Achi é yuku to,
Yemma ga niramu;

---

¹ The name *na* is given to several different kinds of vegetables; but the Japanese turnip is probably here referred to. — This song is sung in nearly all parts of Japan.

Kochi é kuru to,
Yurushité yaru zo.

— If you go that way,[1] Yemma [*or* Emma] will glare at you ! — if you come this way, I promise to forgive you !

(*Dragon-fly-song* — *Tōkyō.*)

Shio ya !
Kané ya !
Yamma kaësé ![2]

Salt Dragon-fly ! — Black Dragon-fly ! — give us back the Big Dragon-fly !

(*Snail-song* — *Tōkyō.*)

Maimaitsubura !
O-yuya no maë ni
Kenkwa ga aru kara
Tsuno dasé, yari dasé !

O snail ! there is a fight in front of the bath-house: so put out your horns, put out your spears !

---

[1] Yama, King of Death.
[2] This song is very old.   Some account of the insects referred to will be found in the preceding paper on dragon-flies !

(Frog-song — Tōkyō.)

Kaëru ga
Naku kara kaërō !

Since the frogs are crying, I shall take leave.[1]

(Snail-song — Province of Shinano.)

Tsubu, tsubu, yama é yuké.
— Orya iya da ! — waré yuké !
Kyonen no haru mo ittaréba,
Karasu to mōsu kurodori ga,
Achi é tsutsuki tsun-mawashi,
Kochi é tsutsuki tsun-mawashi ; —
Ni-do to yukumai ano yama é !

— River-snail, river-snail, go to the mountain ! — I ? not
I ! Go yourself if you want to ! When I went there in the
spring of last year, the black bird that is called " crow "
pecked me and turned me over on one side, and then pecked
me again and turned me over on the other side. Not twice
do I go to that mountain !

*(Song about the cicada called Tsuku-tsuku-bōshi[2] — Province
of Chikuzen.)*

Tsuku-tsuku-bō-San na,
Nanyu naku ka ? —

---

[1] In this little song there is a play on the word *kaëru,* which, as
pronounced, might mean either " to return " or " frog." *Kaërō* is a
future form of the verb.

[2] See article " Sémi " in my *Shadowings,* for some account of this
curious insect.

Oya ga nai ka?
Ko ga nai ka ?
— Oya mo gozaru,
Ko mo gozaru ;
Oitoshi tonogo wo
Mottaréba,
Takajo ni torarété ;
Kyō nanuka.
Nanuka to omoëba —
Shijiu-ku nichi!
Shijiu-ku nichi no
Zeni-kané wo
Dōshité tsukōtana
Yokarō ka ?
Takai komé kōté,
Funé ni tsumu ;
Yasui komé kōté,
Funé ni tsumu.
Funé wa, doko funé ?
Ōsaka-buné.
Ōsaka-buné koso
Né ga yokéré.

— Tsuku-tsuku-bō-San, wherefore do you cry? Have
you no parents ? — have you no children ? — Parents I have,
children also I have; but my good husband was snatched
away from me by a falconer; and to-day is the seventh day

since his death.   Nay — I thought it was the seventh day, —
it is already the forty-ninth ! [1]   What will be the best way
to spend the money of the forty-ninth day ? — Buying dear
rice, to freight a ship ; — buying cheap rice, to freight a ship.
— As for the ship, where is it from ? — It is an Ōsaka ship.
— Ah ! the cost of an Ōsaka ship is indeed very high !

III

MISCELLANEOUS PLAY–SONGS

OF play-songs, — songs to be sung with various out-door or in-door games, — the number is
very great : my own collection includes upwards
of two hundred pieces.   Some take the form of
stories ; others, of dialogues ; others belong to
that class which the French call *chanson énu-
mérative,* or *randonnée :* a few are impossible to
classify.   And some of the most remarkable are
so very queer, — so utterly unlike anything sung
by Western children, — that any translation of
them would remain, even with the aid of a
multitude of notes, unintelligible to readers unfamiliar with Japanese life.   But I think that
the following series of examples will sufficiently

---

[1] There is a reference here to the Buddhist services for the dead
held on the seventh and forty-ninth days after interment.

serve to indicate the oddity and the variety of
this category of child-songs.

(Sung to a crying child.)

Naki-mushi! ké-mushi!
Hasandé sutérō!

Cry-Insect! — Hairy-Insect! [*i. e., Caterpillar*] — with a
pair of chop-sticks we will throw you out of doors! [1]

(Sung to a child afraid of being away from home.)

Inoru! inoru!
Inagasaki ni oni ga iru!
Ato miriya ja ga iru!

Wants to go home! — wants to go home! On the
going-home way [2] a demon is waiting; and if you look
behind you will see a dragon!

(Dance-song.)

Rengé no hana hiraita,
Hiraita, hiraita!
Hiraita to omōtara
Yatokosa to tsubonda!

---

[1] Alluding to the Japanese method of catching and removing a
centipede, caterpillar, or other unpleasant visitor, with a pair of iron
chop-sticks, or fire-tongs.

[2] There is a play upon words here not possible to render in English.

The Lotos-flower has opened, has opened, has opened ! —
Even as I thought that it had opened, — lo ! *yatokosa !* — it
has closed up again ! [1]

(Play-song.)

Uméboshi-San
To iu hito wa,
Ashi kara kao madé
Shiwa-yotté ! —
               Shiwa-yotté !
Aré wa sui,
Koré wa sui, —
               Sui, sui, sui !

The person called Mr. Pickled-Plum is wrinkled all over
from feet to face, — wrinkled all over !   Sour on that side !
sour on this side ! — sour, sour, sour !

(Play-song.)

Chinkan-chinkara !
Kajiya no ko ;
Hadaka dé tobidasu,
Furoya no ko [2] . . .

---

[1] This Song of the Lotos is sung by a company of children who
form a circle, or dancing-round, all holding hands, and facing inwards.
As the song begins the circle is slowly widened ; but at the word
yatokosa all run in together, — closing up the round with a simultaneous
pull.

[2] This appears to be a fragment of some "enumerative song," in
which different trades and occupations are referred to.

Clink ! clank ! — the child of the blacksmith !
Jumping out naked — the child of the bath house !

(Play-song.)

" Kaji-don !   Kaji-don !
Hi hitotsu gosharé ! "
" Hi wa nai, nai ya !
Ano yama koëté,
Kono yama koëté,
Hi wa koko, koko ni aru ! "

"Sir Smith !   Sir Smith !
Please give us a little fire."
"Fire I have none, none at all.
Crossing over that mountain,
Crossing over this mountain,
Fire then you will find here." [1]

(Dance-song.)

Naka no, naka no
Kobotoké wa,
Nazé mata kaganda ?
Oya no hi ni
Ébi tabété,

---

[1] This song is sung in accompaniment to an ingenious and difficult finger-play, — not altogether unlike our nursery-game of "*Dance, Thumbkin, dance !*" — but much more complicated ; both hands being used.

Soré de mata
Kaganda.

—The little Buddha in the middle [*of the dancing-circle*],
the little Buddha in the middle,—why does he remain thus
always bent?—On the anniversary of his parents' death,
he ate shrimps:[1] therefore he remains thus always bent.

(*Another version.*)

Mawari, mawari no
Kobotoké wa,
Nazé sé ga hikui?
Oya no hi ni
Toto kutté,
Soré dé sé ga
Hikui sō na.

—The little Buddha in the middle of the dancing-round,
the little Buddha in the middle,—why is his stature thus
low?—Having eaten fish upon the anniversary of his
parents' death, therefrom his stature remains low.

(*Centipede-dance — Province of Kii.*)

Yurasu ya mukadé!
Atama wa cha-usu;
O wa hiko-hiko yo!

---

[1] On the anniversary of a parent's death, and during the Festival of
the Dead, no good Buddhist should eat fish of any kind.

The centipede moves — shivery-shaky !   The head is like a rice-mortar; — the tail goes *hiko-hiko* [wiggle-waggle] ! [1]

(*Dance-song — Izumo.*)

Jizō-San !   Jizō-San !
Omaë no mizu-wo
Dondo to kundé,
Matsu-ba ni irété,
Makkuri-kaëta ! [2]

Jizō-San, Jizō-San ! plentifully drawing the water of your well, round and round we stir it with pine-leaves, until it spills over.

(*Hand-play song.*)

Ichi ga saita,
Ni ga saita,
San ga saita,
Shi ga saita,
Go ga saita,

---

[1] This Centipede-Dance is performed by a number of children in line, — each grasping the girdle of the one before him ; while the leader holds in his hand some object shaped like a tea-mortar, to represent the centipede's head.   The real tea-mortar would probably prove much too heavy for the sport.

[2] This is usually sung by little girls.   The singers at first stand face to face, in couples, holding hands as they sing.   At the words " *makkuri-kaëta,*" they turn about, without loosing the clasp, so as to come back to back.

Roku ga saita,
Shichi ga saita,
Hachi ga saita,
*Ku*mabachi ga saita,
*Tō*kagé ga saita!

One stings! [here one child lays his right hand upon the right hand of a playfellow] — *two* stings! [left hand upon the right] — *three* stings! [left hand upon the left] — *four* stings! [undermost right hand brought up and laid on] — *five* stings! [same manœuvre by the other player] — *six* stings! — *seven* stings! — the BEE[1] stings! [here the one whose hand is uppermost pinches the other's hand] — the WASP stings! [retaliation] — the LIZARD bites! [a very hard pinch.]

(Game-song.)

"Koko wa doko no hoso-michi ja?"
"Tenjin-San no hoso-michi ja."
"Chotto tōshité kudanshansé!"
"Goyō no nai mono tōshimasénu."
"Tenjin-San é gwan-kakété,
Ofuda osamé ni mairimasu."
"Omaë no uchi wa doko jaina?"
"Hakoné no o-séki degozarimas."
"Sonnara tōyaré, tōyaré!

---

[1] *Hachi*, as pronounced, may mean either "eight" or "bee."

Yuki wa yoi-yoi
Kaëri wa kowai! "

"This narrow road, where does it go?" — "This narrow
road is the Road of the God Tenjin." — "I pray you, allow
me to pass for a moment." — "No one must pass who has
no business to pass." — "Having made a vow to the God
Tenjin, I want to pass to present an *ofuda*." [1] — "Where is
your house?" — "My house is at the barrier [2] of Hakoné."
— "Pass, then! pass! Going, all will be well for you;
but coming back you will have reason to be afraid."

(*Game-song — Izumo.*)

"Kona ko yoi ko da!
Doko no ko da?"
"Tonya Hachibei no otomusumé."
"Nanto yoi ko da!
Kiyō na ko da!
Kiyō ni sodatété
Kita hodo ni
Oya ni jikkwan,
Ko ni go kwan,
Semété O-Baba ni
Shijiu-go kwan."

---

[1] *Ofuda*, a holy text, either written on paper, or stamped upon wood.
[2] *Hakoné no seki*. There used to be a military guard-house at
Hakoné, where all travellers had to give an account of themselves
before proceeding further.

"Shijiu-go kwan no o-kané wo
Nani ni suru?"

"Yasui komé kōté,
Funé ni tsumi:
Funé wa shirokané,
Ro wa kogané.
Saasā osé-osé
Miyako madé."

"Miyako modori ni
Nani morota?"

"Ichi-ni kōgai,
Ni-ni kagami,
San-ni sarasa no
Obi morota."

"Kukété kudasaré,
O-Baba San!"

"Kukyō — kukyō,
To omoëdomo,
Obi ni michikashi,
Tasuki ni nagashi."

"Yamada Yakushi no
Kané no o ni."

—"This child is a fine child!—whose child is she?"—
"She is the youngest daughter of Hachibei, the wholesale
merchant."—"O what a fine child! O what a clever
child! Because she has been so well brought up, I shall

give to the parents ten *kwan*,[1] and to the child five *kwan*, and to the grandmamma not less than forty-five *kwan*." — " With so much money as forty-five *kwan*, what will you do ? " — " Cheap rice I will buy, and load it on a boat. The boat is of silver; the oar is of gold. . . *Saasā!* [' Hearty now ! '] — row hard till we get to the Capital ! " — " What presents have you brought us on your return from the Capital ? " — " Firstly, a hair-pin of tortoise-shell. Secondly, a mirror. Thirdly, a girdle of *sarasa*." [2] — " Please sew it, grandmamma." — " Though I thought to sew it, — though I thought to sew it, it is too short for a girdle; it is too long for a *tasuki* [3]-cord." — " Then I will offer it up as a bell-rope for the bell of [the temple of] Yakushi [4] at Yamada."

(*Game-song.*)

" Kozō, kozō !
Ko hitori gosharé ! "
" Dono ko ga hoshikéra ? "
" Ano ko ga hoshii wa."
" Nani soété yashinau ? "

---

[1] One *kwan* was equal to a thousand copper-cash in old times. — The value of the present given to the grandmother reminds one of the fact that, in a Japanese family, the early training of the children is usually left to the grandparents, and especially to the grandmother.

[2] *Sarasa* is a kind of calico, or chintz.

[3] *Tasuki*, a cord used to tie back the long sleeves of the Japanese robe, during working-hours.

[4] *Yakushi* is the Japanese form of the name *Bhaishagyaraga*. (*Bhaishagyaraga* literally signifies " The Medical King.") Yakushi, or *Yakushi-Nyōrai*, is a very popular Buddhist divinity in Japan, — and is especially prayed to as a healing Buddha.

"Tai soété yashinau."

"Soré wa honé ga atté ikénu."

"Sonnara tai ga honé nara,
Ika soété yashinau."

"Soré wa mushi no dai-doku."

"Sonnara Tono-San no nikai dé
Mōsén shiite ténarai sashozō."

"Té ga yogorété ikénu."

"Sonnara Tono-San no nikai dé
Mōsén shiité satō mochi."

"Sonnara yaruzō!"

"Acolyte, acolyte, please give me one child!" — "Which child do you wish to have?" — "That child I want to have." — "With what kind of food will you feed the child?" — "With *tai*-fish I will feed the child." — "That will not do, — there are too many bones." — "Then, as there are too many bones in *tai*-fish, I will feed the child with cuttle-fish." — "That would be very bad for the stomach of the child." — "Then, in the house of the lord, upstairs, I will spread a rug, and teach the child to write." — "That will not do: it would make the child's hands dirty." — "Then in the house of the lord, upstairs, I will spread a rug, and give sugar-cakes to the child." — "Very well, I will let you have the child."

(New-Year Song.)

Senzō ya! manzō!
O-funé ya gichiri ko,

Gichiri, gichiri, kogéba,
O-Ébisu ka? Daikoku ka?
Kocha fuku no kami!

A thousand ships! ten thousand ships! Hear the
August [*Treasure-*] Ship coming, — *gichiri, gichiri, gichiri*,
as they row! Is it the God Ebisu? is it the God Daikoku?
— Hither come the Gods of Good Fortune.

(*Old Tōkyō Songs of the Bon-Festival.*)

I

Bon no jiu-roku nichi
A-sobasénu oya wa,
Ki-Butsu, Kana-Butsu,
Ishi-Botoké!
Ishi-Botoké!

The parents who will not let their children play on the
sixteenth day of the [*month of the*] Bon-Festival, — they are
wooden Buddhas, — they are metal Buddhas, — they are
Buddhas of stone, Buddhas of stone!

II

Bon, Bon, Bon no
Jiu-roku nichi,
O-Emma Sama yé
Maërō to shitara,
Zuzu no o ga kirété,

Hanao ga kirété,
Namu Shaka Nyōrai!
Té dé ogamu,
Té dé ogamu!

If we go to [*visit the temple of*] the August Lord Emma,[1] on the sixteenth day of the Bon, Bon, Bon, the string of the praying beads having been broken, and the thong of the sandal having been burst, *Namu Shaka Nyōrai!*[2] [*we cry*], — and pray with hands joined, and pray with hands joined.

III

" O-Bon ga kita kara
Kamiyuté okuré."
" Shimada ga yoi ka?
Karako ga yoi ka?"
" Shimada mo iya yo!
Karako mo iya yo!
O-Édo dé hayaru
O-sagé-gami!"

" Now that the Bon-festival has come, please to dress my hair." — " Will the *Shimada*-style[3] suit you? — or will

---

[1] *Yama*, the King of Death. His festival is held on the 16th day of the 7th month, after the three days' Festival of the Dead, — usually called the *Bon*.

[2] " Hail to the Tathâgata, Sakyamuni! " — an invocation uttered, by the members of certain Buddhist sects, on all occasions of distress. — It is believed to be a bad omen for the thong of one's sandal to break.

[3] The *Shimada*-style is the fashion in which a bride's hair is dressed.

the *Karako*[1] style suit you?" — "No, I will not have my hair dressed in the *Shimada*-style, nor will I have it dressed in the *Karako* style. The honorable *sagé-gami*[2] style is now the fashion in the noble city of Yedo."

IV

Ichi no maru koëté,
Ni no maru koëté,
San no maru saki yé
Hori-ido hotté,
Hori wa, hori-ido:
Tsurubé wa kogané;
Kogané no saki yé
Tombō ga tomatté;
Yaré, soré tombō!
Soré, soré tombō!
Tobanakya hané wo
Kirigirisu!
Kiriko ga tōrō,
Kiriko ga tōrō!
Kiriko ga tōrō wa,
Donata no saiku?

[1] The *Karakowagé* was an old-fashioned style of coiffure, — probably as the name implies, of Chinese origin ; the literal meaning of the term being "Chinese-child-coiffure."

[2] The term *sagé-gami* means loose-flowing hair. Anciently noble ladies wore their hair thus.

O-Akashi Sama no
O-té zaiku,
O-té zaiku!

Crossing the innermost line of fortification [1], — crossing the second line of fortification, — at the end of the third line of fortification dug a well, a moat and a well. — The well-bucket is of gold. On the top of the golden bucket a dragon-fly alighted. Oh! that dragon-fly! that dragon-fly! If it does not fly, its wings shall be cut off. [2] — O the *kiriko*-lanterns! [3] — O the *kiriko*-lanterns — who made the *kiriko*-lanterns? Our august Lord Akashi made them with his own august hand, with his own august hand.

V

Nagai, nagai,
Ryōgoku-bashi nagai!
Nagai Ryōgoku-bashi
Suzumi ni détara,
O-ko-sama-gata ga
Yakata no funé dé,
Hikuya, kataruya,
Yaré omoshiroya,

---

[1] The lines of defence about a Japanese castle are counted from within outwards.

[2] There is here an untranslatable play of words, — the term *kiri-girisu*, which is the name of a cricket, being used for the verb *kiri*, to cut.

[3] This is given to a kind of four-sided or polygonal lantern.

Yaré omoshiroya !
Bon-odori !

Long, long,—the Ryōgoku bridge is long. Had you gone there to get cool, on the long Ryōgoku bridge, oh ! to see the honorable children in the pleasure-boats, and to hear the musicians, and the reciters ! — how pleasant it was, how pleasant ! — and the festival dance, too, — the Bon-Odori !

VI

Yanagi no shita no
Oshidori-Sama wa
Asahi ni terarété,
O-iro ga kuroi ;—
O-iro ga kurokirya
Ganguri-gasa o-sashi.
Ganguri-gasa iya yo !
Ganguri-gasa iya yo !
O-Édo dé hayaru
Ja-no-mé-gasa,
Ja-no-mé-gasa !

Under the willow-tree
Sir Mandarin-duck
Being shone upon by the morning sun,
His honorable color is dark.
If the honorable complexion be dark,

Spread a *ganguri*-umbrella.[1]
A *ganguri*-umbrella I will not have !
A *ganguri*-umbrella I will not have !
Now in the honorable city of Yedo, is fashionable
The Serpent's-Eye-umbrella,[2]
The Serpent's-Eye-umbrella.

VII

Konata no yashiki wa
Kirei na yashiki, —
Oku no ma dé samisen,
Naka no ma dé odori wo,
Daidoko ma demo
Fué taiko ! fué taiko !

This residence of yours is a fine residence, — with a
samisen playing in the best back-room, and dancing going
on in the middle-room, and even in the kitchen a flute and
drum, a flute and drum !

(*Tōkyō play-song.*)

" Ōyama no,
Ōyama no

---

[1] *Ganguri-gasa.* I do not know what kind of umbrella was thus
called.

[2] A paper umbrella painted black, all but a band some four or five
inches from the top, so that when the umbrella is opened, this white
ring with the black space which it encloses, resembles in form a serpent's eye.

O-Kon San wa
Doko ittaka ? ”
“ Tonari é
O-imo tabéni ikimashita.”
“ Ō-okashii ! ō-okashii ! ”

“ O-Kon San of Oyama — where has she gone?” —
“ She went next door, to eat some potatoes.” — “ How
very, very strange ! — how very, very strange ! ” [1]

(*Tōkyō play-song.*)

Mukō no yama no
Sumotori-bana wa
Enyaraya to hikéba,
O-té-té ga kiréru, —
O-té-té no kiréta
O-kusuri nai ka ?
Aka no mo aru,
Shiroi no mo aru.
Onaji-ku naréba
Akai no ni shō yo !

When [*with a cry of*] *Enyaraya !* we pull the violets [2] of
yonder mountain, our hands get torn. — Is there no medi-

---

[1] This song belongs to a game of hide-and-seek, played by girls.

[2] Literally, the “ wrestler's-flower,” — so called because of a game
played with violet-flowers. Two children each take a violet, twist the
heads of their flowers together, and pull the stalks in opposite directions until one of them breaks. The player whose violet breaks first is

cine for the torn hand? Red medicine there is, and also white. — If the two medicines are equally good, then I shall certainly take the red.

(Dialogue Song — Province of Izumo.)

" Mukō no yama no
Kawazu ga naku ga !
Nashité naku ka ?
Samuté naku ka ?
Himoji té naku-ka ?
Himojikya ta tsukuré."
" Ta tsukuriya kitanai."
" Kitanakya araë."
" Arauya tsumétai."
" Tsumétakya ataré."
" Atarya atsui."
" Atsukya shizaré."
" Shizara nomi ga kū."
" Nomi ga kūya korosé."
" Korosha kawai ! "
" Kawaikya daiténé."
" Daiténérya nomi ga kū."
" Nomi ga kūya korosé." . . .
&c., &c.

---

the loser. Perhaps the reader will be reminded of our " wishing-bone " sport; but in the Japanese play the flowers are supposed to represent wrestlers.

" The frogs of yonder mountain cry. Why do they cry? Is it for cold that they cry? Is it for hunger that they cry? If you are hungry, till the rice-field." — " It is dirty work, to till the rice-field." — " If it be dirty work, wash." — " It is cold, to wash." — " If it be cold, warm yourselves by the fire." — " It is too hot by the fire." — " If it be too hot, go further away." — " If we go further away, the fleas will bite us." — " If the fleas bite you, kill them." — " It is too pitiful to kill the poor things." — " If you pity them so much, embrace them, and sleep with them." — " If we embrace the fleas and sleep with them, they will bite us." — " If the fleas bite you, kill them," &c., &c.

By far the strangest thing in this part of my collection is a kind of metaphysical dialogue, chanted by children as a play-song! It probably survives from the period when the teaching of children was chiefly intrusted to the Buddhist priesthood, and when almost every Buddhist temple was also a school, or had some kind of a school attached to it. There is nothing very remarkable about the composition itself: it is only the choice of subject — an astonishing subject for a play-song, — that makes the thing seem strange to a Western mind.

This subject is the infinity of Jizō Bosatsu (the Bodhisattva Kshitigarbha), whose smiling images may be seen by almost every roadside, and in

countless Buddhist cemeteries. Often at cross-
roads, and still more often in graveyards, you will
find, instead of a single statue of Jizō, six images
in a row, — each figure bearing a different mys-
tical emblem.   These Six Jizō, or *Roku-Jizō*,
symbolize the teaching that Jizō Bosatsu, self-
multiplied, at once exercises his saving pity in all
the Six Spheres of Sentient Existence, — that is
to say throughout the entire Universe of Forms.
But, according to the higher Buddhism, " there is
no being besides Buddha, and no Buddha besides
being."   All the Buddhas and the Bodhisattvas
are veritably but One ; — all substance, all life,
all mind is but One.   And Jizō of the Six States
of Existence is not only a multiple manifestation
of the Absolute : he also *is* the Absolute. . . .
To find these conceptions embodied in a child's
play-song is somewhat startling ; but there are
many things quite as startling to be met with in
the old popular literature of Buddhism : —

(*Province of Mutsu.*)

Hashi no shita ni Roku-Jizō
Nezumi ni atama wo kajirarété,
— Nezumi koso Jizō da !
— Nezumi Jizō dara,

Nanishini neko ni torarébéna?
— Neko koso Jizō yo!
— Neko wa Jizō dara,
Nanishini inu ni torarébéna?
— Inu koso Jizō yo!
— Inu wa Jizō dara,
Nanishini ōkami ni torarébéna?
— Ōkami koso Jizō yo!
— Ōkami Jizō dara,
Nanishini hi ni makarébéna?
— Hi koso Jizō yo!
— Hi wa Jizō dara,
Nanishini mizu ni késarébéna?
— Mizu koso Jizō yo!
— Mizu wa Jizō dara,
Nanishini hito ni nomarébéna?
— Hito koso Jizō yo!
— Hito wa Jizō dara,
Nanishini Jizō ogamubéna?
— Hon no Jizō wa Roku-Jizō.

— The heads of the Six Jizō under the bridge have been gnawed by some rat. — But that rat itself is really Jizō. — If the rat be Jizō, how comes it that the rat is caught by a cat? — The cat itself is really Jizō. — If the cat be Jizō, how does it happen that the cat is worried by a dog? — Truly the dog itself is also Jizō. — If the dog be Jizō, how explain the fact that it is captured by a wolf? — The wolf

itself is certainly Jizō. — If the wolf be Jizō, why should it
be overcome by fire? — The fire indeed is also Jizō. — If
the fire be Jizō, why should it be extinguished by water? —
The water also is really Jizō. — If the water be Jizō, how
explain the fact that it is drunk by mankind? — Mankind
is really Jizō. — If mankind be Jizō, why should mankind
pray to Jizō? — The true Jizō is the Jizō of the Six States
of Existence (lit., " *the true Jizō is the Six-Jizō* ").

IV

NARRATIVE–SONGS

(*Province of Chōshi.*)

Ora ga tonari no Semmatsu wa,
Ōmi no ikusa ni tanomarété,
Ichi-nen tatté mo mada konai,
Ni-nen tatté mo mada konai,
San-nen tattara kubi ga kita.

As for my neighbor Semmatsu,
Having been engaged for the war in Ōmi,
Though one year passed, still he did not come back;
Though two years passed, still he did not come back:
When three years had passed, his head came back.[1]

(*Province of Izumo.*)

Mukō no yama ni
Saru ga sambiki tōmatté;

---

[1] Cut off, we must suppose.

Maë no saru wa mono shirazu ;
Ato no saru mo mono shirazu ;
Naka no ko-zaru yō mono shitté.
Gozaré tomodachi, hana-mi ni yuko ya ?
Hana wa doko bana ?
Jizō no maë no sakura-bana.
Hito-éda oréba, patto chiru ;
Futa-éda oréba, patto chiru ;
Mi-éda ga saki ni hi ga kurété.
Dochi no kōya é yado toroka ?
Higashi no kōya é yado toroka ?
Minami no kōya é yado toroka ?
Tonosan no kōya é yado totté,
Tatami wa mijikashi, yo wa nagashi.
Akazuki okité sora mitara
Gikko no bakko no kiisengo.
Funédomo saraëté ho wo kakétsu.
Hokakébuné no tsuri-mono wa,
Shiro-ori, aka-ori, aka-ji no
Majitta tsuba-katana.

In yonder mountain three monkeys dwell. The first
monkey knows nothing. The last monkey also knows
nothing. But the midmost little monkey knows everything well. — Come, friends, let us go to see the flowers.
—Flowers ? where are the flowers ?—Before the statue
of Jizō the cherry-flowers are blooming. As I break one

branch, the cherry-flowers fall scattering. As I break a
second branch the cherry-flowers fall scattering. Before I
can break a third, the darkness comes. — In what dye-house
shall I find lodging? Shall I take lodging in the eastern
dye-house? Shall I take lodging in the southern dye-
house? — Lodging in the dye-house of the Tono-Sama
(*lord*), the mats I find short, and the night long. — Awaking
at dawn, if I see the sky . . . .[1], cleaning out the ships,
hoisting the sails. The sails of this sailing-ship are of white
cloth and red; the rigging is of red silk cord from the
variegated hilts of swords.[2]

(*Province of Izumo.*)

Yaré haratatsu! — tatsu naraba;
Suzuri to fudé to o-té ni motté,
Omou koto wo kaki-oïté,
Murasaki-ga é mi wo nagéta.
Shita kara zako ga tsutsuku yara,
Uĕ kara karasu ga tsutsuku yara.
Tsutsuita karasu wa doko yukita?
Mori-ki no shita é mugi maki ni.
Nan-goku, nan-goku maité kita?
Ni-sen-goku maité kita.

---

[1] Here is a line of which I could not obtain a translation, — *gikko no
bakko no kiisengo*. Perhaps the text is corrupt.

[2] This is not quite literal; but it is certainly the original meaning of
the description. — There are a great many songs of the same kind.
Might not the kind be described as an imperfect form of *randonnée*, —
a *randonnee* in the first stage of evolution?

Ni-sen-goku no nō ni wa
Téra no maë dé ko wo unda.
Jūji no koromo é chi ga tsuité,
Amé-taré-mizu dé aratté,
Kōro no hi dé abutté;
Kōro no hi ga taraidé,
Abura-hi dé abutté;
Abura-hi ga taraidé,
Kudo no hi dé abutté;
Kudo no hi ga taraidé,
Kotatsu no hi dé abutté.

What ! you are angry ? Ah ! if you be angry, taking
inkstone and writing-brush in your honorable hand, think
of what you wish to write and to leave behind you ! [1]
When you have cast your body into the Purple River
[*Murasaki-gawa*] small fishes will nibble it from below;
crows will pick it from above. — The crow that picked,
where is it gone? — It has gone under a forest-tree, to sow
wheat. — How many *koku*,[2] how many *koku* have been
sown ? — Two thousand *koku* have been sown. — By reason
of the sowing of two thousand *koku*, a child is born in
front of the temple. — The upper robe of the chief priest
having been sprinkled with blood, he washed it in rain-
water, and dried it by the fire of a censer.   The fire in the
censer being insufficient, he dried it by fire of oil.   The fire
of oil being insufficient, he dried it by the fire of a cook-

---

[1] Alluding to the custom of writing a letter to explain one's motives,
before suicide.

[2] One *koku* is equal to about 5.13 bushels.

ing-range. The fire of the cooking-range being insufficient,
he dried it by the fire of a *kotatsu*.[1]

(*Province of Isé.*)

Néko ga Kuwana é mairutoté;
Kuwana no michi dé hi ga kiété,
Toboshitémo, toboshitémo, toboraidé.
Chaya no en éto koshikakété,
— Mizu wo ippai okurenka ?
— Mizu wo yaru no wa yasui kédo,
Tsurubé no soko ga nukémashita.
— Yaré, yaré ! kitsui ané-san ja !
O-cha wo ippuku okurenka ?
— O-cha wo yaru no wa yasui kédo,
Chagama no soko ga nukémashita.
— Yaré, yaré ! kitsui ané-san ja !
Tabako wo ippuku okurenka ?
— Tabako yaru no wa yasui kédo,
Kiséru no kubi ga nukémashita.

---

[1] A *kotatsu* is a square structure ; the sides and top being formed by
wooden bars ; and the lower part containing a metal brasier, or warming-
pan, in which a charcoal fire is lighted. Over this structure heavy
quilts are thrown ; and a number of persons can keep themselves warm
by sitting round the *kotatsu* with their knees under the quilts. The size
of the *kotatsu* varies from about one foot to two feet square. Diction-
aries absurdly describe the thing as " a kind of hearth." It is not a
hearth ; but in Western Japan it occupies a place in the home like that
of the hearth with us, — for the family assemble about it of winter
evenings.

—Yaré, yaré! kitsui ané-san ja! . . .
Hi — fu — mi — yo — itsu — mu — nana —
ya — kono — to !

A cat set out for Kuwana.   On the road to Kuwana her
light went out.   Though she tried and tried to relight it,
she could not.   Then, having seated herself on the veranda
of a tea-house, she asked : — "One cup of water will you
not kindly give me?" — "It would be very easy to give
you water ; but the bottom of the well-bucket has been
taken out." — "Oh ! oh ! how harshly speaks this Elder
Sister ! [1]   Then will you not kindly give me a cup of tea?"
— "To give you some tea were an easy matter; but the
bottom of the tea-kettle has been taken out." — "Oh ! oh !
how merciless this Elder Sister !   Then will you not let
me have one pipeful of tobacco ?" — "To give you some
tobacco were an easy matter; but the bowl of the pipe has
fallen off " — "Oh ! oh ! what a merciless Elder Sister ! "
— *One — two — three — four — five — six — seven —*
eight —nine — ten ! [2]

Of course the cat, in the foregoing narration,
is a goblin-cat, — a cat having power to assume
divers shapes.   She travels in human form ; but
this disguise is penetrated by the eye of the tea-
house servant, who answers her as goblins are

---

[1] "Elder Sister" is still the title of courtesy by which the maid-ser-
vant of an inn is addressed; but the form *Nésan*, a contraction of *Ané-
san*, is more frequently used.

[2] The numbers here refer to a game played to the accompaniment of
the song.

answered. . . . If any goblin or ghost ask you
for a bucket or other vessel, it is better not to refuse directly ; but you must be careful to knock
the bottom out of the vessel asked for before
yielding it up, — otherwise the consequences
might be fatal.

This reminds me of a superficial criticism
sometimes made in regard to those European
fairy-tales which recount the wooing of beautiful
maidens by frogs or birds, and the intermarriage
of different species of animals. It has been said
that the monstrous absurdity of such stories un-
fits them for the perusal of children, and, further-
more, deprives them of all artistic merit. But
most of these fairy-tales can be traced back to
Oriental sources ; and to the Oriental mind there
is nothing absurd in the idea of marriage between human and non-human beings, — since it
is believed that many animals can assume human
shapes at will. To Far-Eastern faith all life is
One ; and the forms that enclose it but temporary conditions. Without some knowledge of
Far-Eastern beliefs,[1] the real charm of the old

---

[1] The beliefs are older than Buddhism ; but Buddhism
gave them considerable recognition. One of the questions

Japanese fairy-tales cannot be understood. In any event they should be read in translation only when illustrated by Japanese artists. The illustrations will explain much that the bare text leaves in mystery.

In the next song we have the story of a serpent assuming the shape of a certain man's daughter. Stories of serpent-women and dragon-women abound in Japanese literature. Probably both this song and the preceding one were inspired by the memory of some old romance or drama: —

(*Province of Shinano.*)

Mukō no ozawa ni ja ga tatté, —
Hachiman-Chōja no oto-musumé.
Yoku mo tattari takundari,
Té ni wa nihon no tama wo mochi,
Ashi ni wa kogané no kutsu·wo haki,
Ā yobé, kō yobé, to iinagara,
Yama kuré no kuré ittaréba,
Kusakari tonogo ni yukiatte,
— Obi wo kudasaré, tonogo-sama.

---

formerly to be asked of any one desiring to enter the Buddhist Order, according to the Vinaya texts, was this: — "*Are you a human being?*"

— Obi mo kasa mo yasui koto,
Oré no nyōbo ni naru-naraba:
Asa wa okité kami-yūté.
— Hana no saku madé 'nété machi yo!

From the swamp beyond there rose up a serpent, in the likeness of the youngest daughter of the wealthy Hachiman. Well did it assume that form, skilfully standing. Holding in its hands two gems, and wearing upon its feet shoes of gold, it traversed mountains and fields, crying out the while:—" Call there ! — Call here ! " Then did it meet a grass-cutter, and say to him:—" Fair husband, deign to give me a girdle ! " — " To give you [*he answered*] both a girdle and a hat will be easily done, if you become my wife. Then every morning, early rising, I will arrange your hair." — Wait then [*she said*],— patiently wait until the season of the blooming of flowers."

V

BATTLEDOOR–SONGS AND BALL–SONGS

IN the time of the New-Year holidays the streets are made beautiful by groups of young girls playing at battledoor-and-shuttlecock, or at various games of hand-ball. It were difficult to imagine anything more charming than some of these little maids in their long-sleeved and many-colored holiday-costume: only the most radiant of moths or butterflies might serve for a comparison. Very skilful are the Tōkyō artists in portraying the grace and the daintiness of them; and every year these artists delight us with new colored prints of bevies of ball-players — (showing the fashions of the season), — or pictures of some fairy-damsel with upturned smiling face and shining eyes, and flower-lips half-parted, as she watches, battledoor in hand, the feathery missile in its course. Yet the reality may often be much more lovely than the picture. And, oh! what wonderful battledoors are sometimes to be seen! — cushioned at the back with silk mosaic-work, making the dream of a landscape, a garden, a princess of ancient days!

Yet the charm is not visual only; — these fairies, in their play, sing little songs of strange rhythm and melody, very sweet to hear, and (for the Western listener) impossible to remember.

Many of these queer little songs are so constructed that the first syllable of each successive line or phrase corresponds with the first syllable of a numeral noting the ordinal place of the line or phrase. Most commonly the Japanese numerals are used:—*hitotsu, futatsu, mitsu, yotsu, itsutsu, mutsu, nanatsu, yatsu, kokonotsu,* and *tō.* But in various examples the Chinese numerals are used—*ichi, ni, san, shi, go, roku, shichi, hachi, ku, jiu.* And in sundry compositions the two sets of numerals are mixed together. With the utterance of each line or phrase the shuttlecock or the ball ought to be struck once. The term *chō* ("even number") seems usually to signify ten strokes;—but this meaning is not always evident.

(*Tōkyō Battledoor-song.*)

*Hito*ri kina,
*Futa*ri kina,
*Mi*té yukina,
Yotté yukina;
Itsu kité
*Muzu*kashi;
*Nana Ya*kushi,
Koko no ma dé
To yo!

Come, one! come, two!— After seeing, go!— After entering, go!— Whenever I come to see you, your face is

gloomy. — Seven for Yakushi ! [1] — There you are ! — ten
with the stroke of nine !

(*Kyōto Battledoor-song.*)

> *Hito*ri kina,
> *Futa*ri kina,
> *Mi*té yukita,
> *Yo*tté yukina ;
> *Itsu* kité mitémo
> *Nana*ko obi wo
> *Ya*kuruma ni shimété.
> *Kokono* yo dé itchō yo !

Come, one ! Come, two ! — After seeing, departed ; —
after entering, go ! Whenever I come to see you, you
put on your *Nanako* [2]-girdle, tying it in the mode called
" Eight Wheels." With this ninth stroke, one chō is
completed.

(*Kyōto Battledoor-song.*)

> *Hito*mé,
> *Futa*mé,
> *Mi*yakashi,
> *Yo*mégo,
> *Itsu*ya no

---

[1] Yakushi-Nyōrai (*Bhaishagyaràga*), the Healing Buddha.
[2] *Nanako* is the name given to a kind of heavy twilled silk with a
wavy lustre.

Musashi,
Nanaya no
Yatsushi, —
Kokono ya !
Tō !

One eye-glance ! — two glances ! — the August Lights [of the Gods] ! — the Daughter-in-Law ! — the Chequer-game [sold at the shop] Itsuya ! — the dandy [-clerk] of the shop Nanaya ! — Nine there are ! — And ten !

(*Battledoor-song — Province of Shinano.*)

Hi-yara Hikobé ;
Nakané no O-Toyo ;
Sando-mé ni makété,
Abékobé chinchikurin,
Chinchikurin no chinchikurin ;
*Hito*ko ni *futa*go,
*Mi*watasu *yo*mégo,
Itsu kité *mi*témo,[1]
*Nana*ko no obi wo
Ya no ji ni shimété,
Kono ya wo *tō*ru.

There goes one, Hikobé ! — O-Toyo of Nakané ; — three times defeated ; — upside-down now, *chinchikurin !* — *chin-*

---

[1] The syllable *mi* of *mitémo* is here considered to be an equivalent for *mu*, the first syllable of *mutsu*, " six."

chikurin! and *chinchikurin!* — one child and twins; — bride seen far away; whenever I go to see her, she puts on her *Nanako-obi* (taffeta girdle), tying it in the form of the character *Ya*,[1] — and so she passes before this house.

Sometimes the names of ten celebrated temples, or the names of ten divinities, or even the names of the months, are used for the same enumerative purpose, — as in the following examples: —

(*Tōkyō Ball-song.*) [2]

Ichi ni Ichibata O-Yakushi Sama yo !
Ni-niwa Nihon no Nikkō-Sama yo !
San-ni Sanuki no Kompira-Sama yo !
Shi-ni wa Shinano no Zenkōji-Sama yo !
Itsutsu Enoshima Benten-Sama yo !
Roku-ni Rokkakudō no Kwannon-Sama yo !
Nanatsu Nana-ura no Tenjin-Sama yo !
Yatsu Yawata no Hachiman-Sama yo !
Kokonotsu Kōya no Kōbō-Sama yo !
Tō dé tokoro no Ujigami-Sama yo !
Kakéta gwan nara tokanéba naranu !

The first time for the August Lord Yakushi of Ichibata;
The second, for the Lord Deity of Nikkō in Japan;

---

[1] The *Hiragana* character " ya " is here referred to. — This way of tying the girdle is still in fashion, and is still called the " Ya-no-ji " manner.

[2] Variants of this composition seem to be known in almost every part of Japan.

The third, for the Lord Kompira of Sanuki;
The fourth, for the Lord Buddha of Zenkōji in Shinano;
The fifth, for the deity Benten of Enoshima;
The sixth, for the deity Kwannon of the Rokkakudō;
The seventh, for the August Lord Tenjin, of Nana-ura;
The eighth, for the August Lord Hachiman, of Yawata;
The ninth, for the Lord Kōbōdaishi of Kōya;
The tenth, for the tutelary Gods of this place.
The vow that has been made must always be kept !

(*Kyōto Battledoor-song.*)

Shōgwatsu, —
            Kadomatsu ;
Nigwatsu, —
            Hatsu-uma ;
Sangwatsu, —
            Sekku ;
Shigwatsu, —
            O-Shaka ;
Gogwatsu, —
            Nobori ;
Rokugwatsu, —
            Tennō ;
Shichigwatsu, —
            Tanabata ;
Hachigwatsu, —
            Hassaku ;

Kugwatsu, —
> Kiku-tsuki ;

Jiugwatsu, —
> Ebisu-kō ;

Shimotsuki ;
> Shiwasu ;

Kokono yo dé
> Itchō yo !

First Month, Gate-Pinetree;[1] — Second Month, First Day-of-the-Horse;[2] — Third Month, Girls' Festival;[3] — Fourth Month, the August Sâkyamuni;[4] — Fifth Month, Flags;[5] Sixth Month, Festival of the tutelar God;[6] — Seventh Month, Festival of the Weaver;[7] — Eighth Month, Festival of the First Day; — Ninth Month, the Month of Chrysanthemums; — Tenth Month, Festival of Ebisu;[8] — The Frost Month; — The Last Month; — Nine strokes given — now one *chō* is now completed.

---

[1] The *Kadomatsu*, or "Gate-Pine," is planted before the main entrance of a house on the first day of the new year.

[2] This is the great festival of the Rice-God; — the term *Hatsu-uma*, or "First Horse-Day," signifies only seventh day, each day of the old month being named after one of the twelve Signs of the Zodiac.

[3] Also called the Festival of Dolls.

[4] The Birthday of the Buddha is celebrated on the eighth day of the fourth month.

[5] This is the Boys' Festival. *Nobori* are flags, bearing symbolic designs, and are hoisted in celebration of the birth of a son. In Tōkyō paper or cotton figures of carp-fish are used in lieu of *nobori*.

[6] *Tennō* is the name usually given to the guardian-deity of a city or district.

[7] The Weaver is the Star Vega.

[8] Patron-God of Labor.

(*Ball-song — Province of Shinano.*)

Daikoku-Sama, to iu hito wa, —
Ichi-ni, tawara wo funmaëté ;
Ni-ni, nikkori warōté ;
San-ni, sakazuki itadaité ;
Yotsu dé, yo no naka yoi yō ni ;
Itsutsu dé, izumi no waku yō ni ;
Mutsu, mubyō sokusai ni ;
Nanatsu, nanigoto nai yō ni ;
Yatsu dé, yashiki wo tairagété ;
Kokonotsu, ko-kura wo oshitatété ;
Tō dé, tokkuri osamatta.

[*Praying to*] the person called Daikoku-Sama, — firstly,
as he treads upon the rice-bales, — secondly, as he laughs
with pleasant countenance, — thirdly, taking the *saké*-cup
respectfully in hand, — fourthly, — [*we beseech him*] that all
the world may prosper, — fifthly, that the springs may
purely flow, — sixthly, that the people may be free from all
sickness and calamity, — seventhly, that all evils may cease,
— eighthly, that our house may be victorious [*in war*], —
ninthly, that treasure-houses may be erected, — tenthly, that
universal peace may continue to prevail.

This last is a curious example of a prayer transformed into a ball-song.   Excepting the first four
lines the text is almost, word-for-word, the text
of an old samurai-prayer, — the household prayer

which every warrior repeated daily. . . . Some
of the following, on the other hand, are little
more than nonsense-verses : —

(*Battledoor-song — Province of Echizen.*)

> Hi ya !
> Fu ya !
> O-Koma San !
> Tabako no
> Kemuri wa,
> Jōhattsan !

One struck ! — two struck !   O-Koma San !   Smoke of
tobacco — Jōhattsan.[1]

(*Battledoor-song — Province of Shinano.*)

> Ichigwatsu ;
> Nigwatsu ;
> Sangwatsu,
> Sakura ;
> Yanagi no
> Shita dé,

---

[1] *Jōhattsan*, familiar abbreviation of Jōhachi San (" Mr. Jōhachi").
The song alludes to the popular drama entitled " O-Koma-Saiza."
O-Koma, the heroine of this play, is a beautiful girl who comes to an
unhappy end through the rascality of Jōhachi, a trusted servant in her
father's house. Jōhachi appears on the stage, in various scenes of
the drama, squatting before a *hibachi*, and smoking furiously.

Keshō
Shité ; —
Tō
Yo !

The first month; the second month; the third month,
cherry-flowers !   Under the willow-tree, making my toilet
—there goes ten !

(*Battledoor-song — Province of Shinano.*)

Hi ya !
Hikobé !
Hagétaka,
Jirobé ?
Jirobé no
Atama wa,
Nazé hagéta ?
Oya ga
Jakendé,
Hi é kubéta.

One for Hikobé !   How did you get bald, Jirobé ?   As
for Jirobé's head — how did it become bald ?   His parents,
being cruel, put his head in the fire.

(*Kyōto Ball-song.*)

Hi, fu, mi, yo,
Yomo no keshiki wo

Haru to nagamété; —
Umé ni uguisu
" Hō-Hō-Hōkékyō " to saëzuru.
Asu wa Gion no
Niken chaya dé,
Koto ya samisen
Hayashi tenten
Témari-uta,
" Uta no Nakayama "
Chiyo go ni go-jiu dé
Chiyo roku — roku — roku,
Chiyo shichi — shichi — shichi,
Chiyo hachi — hachi — hachi,
Chiyo ku ni ku-jiu dé
Chotto hyaku tsuita.

One, two, three, four ! — in each of the four directions gazing, everywhere the signs of spring are seen. On the plum-tree the nightingale sings *Hō-Hō-Hōkékyō*.[1] To-morrow in the two tea-houses of Gion-street, with accompaniment of *koto* and *samisen* — ting-ting ! — will be sung the hand-ball songs, and the song called " *Uta no Nakayama*." . . . Thus making fifty and five *chiyo*.[2] . . . *Chiyo*, six — six — six ! *Chiyo*, seven — seven — seven ! *Chiyo*, eight —

[1] With regard to the cry of the *uguisu*, see the preceding paper on Buddhist nomenclature.

[2] *Chiyo* is here the same as *cho,* meaning the even number, or full ten.

eight — eight!   *Chiyo*, nine and ninety now! . . . Even so
a hundred have been struck!

(*City of Shidzuoka*.)

Uguisu ya! uguisu ya!
Tama-tama miyako é noboru toki,
Umé no ko-éda ni hiruné shité,
O-Chiyo ni nani-nani kisété yaru?
Uwagi wa kon-kon-kon-chirimen,
Shitagi wa chin-chin-chirimen; —
Soré wo kisété yattaréba
Michi dé korobu ka? — té wo tsuku ka?
Tono-San ga tōtara, o-jigi wo séyo;
Omma[1] kitaraba, waki ni yoré;
Té-narai kodomo wo kamō-nayo;
Kamōto sōshi dé butaréruzo!
Mazu, mazu ikkwan okashimōshita!

— O Nightingale, Nightingale! when some time you go
to the capital, sleeping by day on a plum-tree bough, what
will you give O-Chiyo to wear? — An upper dress of dark-
blue, dark-blue, dark-blue crêpe-silk; an under-dress of rare,
rare, rare crêpe-silk. So dressed, when I send her out,
I shall warn her not to stumble, or to dirty her hands. "If
a Lord passes on the road, [*I shall say to her*,] make the
honorable reverence. If an honorable horse approaches,
keep well to one side of the road. Do not vex the children

---

[1] *Omma* is a corruption of *O-uma*, "honorable horse."

on their way to the writing-school; — if you vex them, you
will certainly be beaten with copy-books." — Now, now I
have lent you one *kwan* [i. e., I have struck the ball one
hundred times !] [1]

(Province of Echizen.)

Hitotsu, hiita mamé, —
      Ko ni shita mamé ;
Futatsu, funda mamé, —
      Tsuburéta mamé ;
Mitsu, miso-mamé, —
      Fukuréta mamé ;
Yotsu, yotta mamé, —
      Kirei na mamé ;
Itsutsu, itta mamé, —
      Hara-kitta mamé ;
Mutsu, murōta mamé, —
      Tokushita mamé ;
Nanatsu, natta mamé,—
      Saya-tsuki mamé ;
Yatsu, yatta mamé, —
      Son-shita mamé ;
Kokonotsu, kōta mamé, —
      Zéni-dashita mamé ;

---

[1] The ancient *kwan* was worth 1000 cash, — or *mon*. Its value was
therefore about the same as that of the dollar of 100 cents.

To dé totta mamé, —
        Nushito-shita mamé.

One — for ground peas, —
      the peas made into flour;
Two, — for trampled peas, —
      the peas which were crushed;
Three, — the peas made into *miso*-sauce, —
      fermented peas;
Four, — the selected peas, —
      the beautiful peas;
Five, — for parched peas, —
      the belly-cut peas;
Six, — for peas given to us, —
      the peas which we gained;
Seven, — for growing peas, —
      the peas in the pod;
Eight, — the peas given away, —
      the peas that are lost;
Nine, — the peas which we paid for, —
      the money-bought peas;
And *Ten*, — for the peas that we took, —
      the stolen peas !

The interest of the next selection — best of all the ball-songs — is of quite another kind. The scheme of the composition is not unlike that of our celebrated nursery-game, " I love my love with an A "; and the narration can be extended or varied indefinitely according to the imaginative wit of the players : —

(*Tōkyō Hand-ball Song.*)

FIRST PLAYER:—

O-Kan — Kan — Kan —
Kaga-Sama yashiki ja,
O-Késa kométsuku,
Konuka ga ochiru.
— Nantoté ochiru?
Sasa! shichiku-dakè!
Sasa! hachiku-dakè!
— Mukō no mukō no
Kōshi-zukuri no
Shirakabé-zukuri no
Akai-noren no kakatta,
O-Himé-Sama madé
O-watashi —
Mōsu-su-su no su!

SECOND PLAYER:—

Ukétotta! ukétotta!
Ukétotta!
Daiji no o-mari wo ukétotta!
Aa! ukétotta!
Chō ya, hana ya to
O-sodatémōshité;
O-kaëshimōshité

Konya no ban kara:
Kami mo irazumi,
Suzuri mo irazumi;
Hari sambon, —
Kinu-ito mi-suji ni, —
Omma ga sambiki, —
O-kago ga sanchō.
Norikaĕ-hik'kaĕ,
Mukō no ʰnukō no
Kōshi-zukuri no
Kaki no noren no
? ——— Sama madé
O-watashi —
Mōsu-su-su no su!

FIRST PLAYER : —

In the residence of the Lord of Ka — Ka — Kaga, the maid O-Késa is cleaning rice, and the rice-bran falls. With what sound does it fall?— With the sound of *Sasa! shichiku-daké!—sasa! hachiku-daké!* [1] . . . Now to the maiden-princess dwelling far, far away,[2] — in the house with the

---

[1] These words are all names of bamboo. The *sasa* is a small variety of bamboo: the *shichiku-daké* is a black bamboo; and the *hachiku-daké* is a purplish bamboo. But in this song the words are used only as onomatopes. The syllables *sasa* represent the creaking of the great wooden mallet, when lifted by the feet of the rice-pounder; and the syllables *shichiku-daké*, *hachiku-daké* are intended to imitate the noise of the mallet falling, and the dull thud of the blow.

[2] *Mukō no mukō* (lit., "in front of in front") might better be rendered by our colloquial phrase, "at the back of beyond."

lattice-work, — in the house with the white walls, — in the house with the red curtains hung up, — I do now most worshipfully this ball pas-s-s-ss !

[Here the ball is thrown to another girl, who catches it, and sings : —]

SECOND PLAYER :—

I have caught it ! I have caught it ! I have received the precious ball. Ah ! I have received it ! Like a butterfly, like a blossom, even so tenderly shall it be honorably cared for; and by this night shall it worshipfully be returned. [To return it] neither paper nor inkstone will be needed,[1] — but three needles, and three lines of silken thread,[2] — and three honorable horses, and three honorable palanquins. . . Changing horses, and again changing horses, [I myself shall carry this ball] to the Lady ———[3] who dwells far, far away from here, — in the building with the lattice-work, in the building with the persimmon-colored curtains hung up. To her I now do worshipfully [this ball] pas-s-s-ss !

VI

LULLABIES

A PARTICULAR psychological interest attaches to the literature of the lullaby, independently of

---

[1] Because the ball will not be returned merely by a messenger bearing a letter of thanks.

[2] Because it will be respectfully enclosed in a silken wrapper or bag.

[3] Here the real name of the girl, to whom the ball is next to be thrown, may be mentioned.

country or race. Being the natural utterance of
mother-love, the lullaby may be said to express
the most ancient form of tender experience; and
in almost every time and place the essential character of this variety of folk-song has been little
affected by social changes of any sort. Whether
narrative or jingle, sense or nonsense, the verses
usually contain some reference to those familiar
things in which the child-mind discovers cause
for wonder: horses or cows, trees or flowers, the
moon and the stars, birds or butterflies, sights of
the street or garden. Often the lullaby represents the reiteration of one term of caress, alter-
nated with promises of reward for docility, and
hints of danger as a result of fretfulness. The
promises commonly refer to food or toys; and
the threatened penalties are not to be inflicted by
the mother, but by some bogey or goblin having
power to punish naughty children. To such
general rules the Japanese lullabies do not offer
any remarkable exceptions; but they abound in
queer fancies, and have a distinctly Oriental
quality.

Perhaps the European reader will be startled by
the apparition of the syllables *nenné* and *nennéko*

at the beginning of these little songs; for many
of the French *berceuses* also begin with the syllables *néné*, having nearly the same sound.
(The French word *néné*, — pronounced in some
dialects *nenna* and *nono*, — is commonly used by
mothers in southern France; *dodo* being the
northern equivalent.[1])   But of course there is no
real etymological relation between the French
néné and the Japanese *nenné*.   The Japanese
phrase, *nennéko*, is compounded with a syllable
of the verb *nèru*, signifying to sleep; a syllable
of the word *nenné* or *nennéi*, meaning baby; and
the word *ko*, meaning child.   " Sleep, baby-
child ! " is the real meaning of the expression.

(*Province of Isé.*)

Nenné, nenné-to !
Neru-ko wa kawai ;
Okité-naku-ko wa
Tsura-nikui.

Sleep, little one, sleep !   Sweet is the face of the sleeping
child; — ugly the face of the wakeful child that cries !

---

[1] See, for examples, M. Tiersot's *Histoire de la Chanson Populaire
en France :* pp. 136-137, *et seq.*

(*Province of Izumo.*)

Nennéko, nennéko, nennéko ya !
Netara o-kaka é tsurété ina !
Okitara gagama ga totté kama !

Sleep, sleep, O sleep, my child ! If you sleep I will go home to fetch your mother ! If you stay awake the *Gagama*[1] will catch and bite you !

(*Kyōto Lullaby.*)

Nétaka ? nénandaka ?
Makura ni toëba,
Makura mono iuta,
Néta to iuta.

Gone to sleep ? — not yet sleeping ? When I questioned the pillow, the pillow spoke words : " Already asleep," — so it said.

(*Province of Musashi.*)

Nennéko ! nennéko !
Nennéko yō !
Oraga akabo wa
Itsu dékita ?

---

[1] This is an Izumo name for some kind of Goblin. I wonder if the term is not a corruption of the ancient word *Gogomé,* — a name given to certain phantoms of the primitive Shintō cult, — the Ugly Women of the Underworld.

San-gwatsu, sakura no
Saku toki ni:
Dōri dé o-kao ga
Sakura-iro.

Sleep, sleep, sleep, my child! When was my baby made? In the third month, in the time of the blooming of cherry-flowers. Therefore the color of the honorable face of my child is the color of the cherry-blossom.

(*Province of Sanuki.*)

Nennen, nennen,
Nennen yō! —
Nennéshita ko ni
Hanéita to hané to;
Nenné-sen ko ni
Hané bakari. . . .

Sleep, sleep, sleep! — For the little one who goes to sleep, a battledoor and shuttlecock! For the child who does not sleep, only a shuttlecock!

(*Province of Shinano.*)

Nennen-yō!
Korokoro yō!
Nennen-Koyama [1] no

---

[1] Perhaps the name *Nennen-Koyama* might be translated, "The Hills of the Land of Nod." The *Kiji*, a beautiful green pheasant, often betrays itself to the hunter by its cry; — hence the proverb, *Kiji mo*

Kiji no ko wa,
Nakuto o-taka ni
Toraréru yō!

Sleep! happily sleep! The young of the *kiji* in the Hill of Nennen — if it cries it is sure to be taken by the hawk.

(*Province of Iᴢumo.*)

Nennéko, nennéko, nennéko ya!
Achira muitémo yama yama;
Kochira muitémo yama yama.
Yama no naka ni nani ga aru?
Shii ya donguri kaya no mi.

Sleep, sleep, little one, sleep! I turn that way; but I see only mountains. I turn this way; but I see only mountains. In the midst of those mountains what can there be? There are *shii*[1]-nuts and acorns and seeds of *kaya*.[2]

(*Province of Iᴢumo.*)

Nennéko sé, nennéko sé!
Nenné no omori wa doko é itta?
Yama wo koëté sato, é itta.

---

nakaᴢuba utaré wa shimai: "If the Kiji did not cry, it would not be shot."

[1] The *shii*-tree is a variety of live-oak.
[2] The *kaya* is a kind of yew.

Sato no miyagé ni nani morota?
Denden-taiko ni furi-tsuzumi,
Okiagarikoboshi ni inu-hariko.

Sleep, little one, sleep! Where is the sleep-nurse, the girl-nurse gone? Over the hills to her own village-home. When she comes back, what presents will she bring you? A round drum to beat and a hand-drum [1] to shake; an *okiagarikoboshi*,[2] and a paper dog.

(*Province of Isé*.)

Nenné sansé yō!
Kyō wa ni-jiu-go nichi;
Asu wa kono ko no
Miya-mairi.
Miya é mairaba
Dō iuté ogamu?
Kono ko ichi-dai
Mamé na yo ni.

Sleep, child! sleep! To-day is the twenty-fifth day. To-morrow morning this child will make his first visit to the [Shintō] parish-temple. When I go with him to the temple, what shall I pray for? I will pray that through all his life this child may be healthy and strong.

----

[1] The round shallow drum is called a *dendem-taiko*. The *tsuzumi* is a hand-drum of a very peculiar shape. Of course the toy-drums here referred to are considerably smaller than the real instrument.

[2] The *okiagarikoboshi* is a little figure of a wrestler which is so weighted as to assume an erect posture, no matter how thrown down.

(*Province of Musashi.*)

Nennéko, nennéko,
Nennéko yō!
Oraga akabō no
Néta rusu ni,
Azuki wo yonagété,
Komé toïdé,
Aka no mamma é
Toto soëté,
Aka no ii-ko ni
Kūréru-zo!

Sleep, sleep, sleep, little one! While my baby sleeps I will wash some red beans and clean some rice; — then adding some fish to the red rice, I will serve it up to this best of little babies.

(*Province of Echizen.*)

Uchi no kono ko no
Makura no moyō,
Umé ni uguisu,
Matsu ni tsuru:
Umé ni narétémo,
Sakura wa iyaya; —
Onaji hana demo,
Chiri yasui.

The designs upon the pillow of this child of the house are nightingales and plum-trees, storks and pines. I am used to the plum-tree-design; but I would not have the cherry-flower design. Though the cherry-tree be equal in beauty to the plum-tree, its blossoms too easily fall.[1]

(*Matsuè : Province of Izumo.*)

Nennéko, nennéko nennéko ya!
Kono ko nashité naku-yara?
O-chichi   ga   taranuka?   — o-mama   ga
   taranuka?
Ima ni ototsan no ōtono no o-kaëri ni
Amé ya, o-kwashi ya, hii-hii ya,
Gara-gara, naguréba fuito tatsu
Okiagarikoboshi! —
Nennéko, nennéko, nennéko ya!

Sleep, sleep, sleep, little one! Why does the child continue to cry? Is the honorable milk deficient? — is the honorable rice deficient? Presently when father returns from the great Lord's palace, *amé* will be given you, and

---

[1] Therefore the design is unlucky. Some local bit of folklore is suggested by this composition; — usually the cherry-flower is thought to be a happy symbol. — In this connection I may observe that the lotos-flower design is held to be unlucky. It is never to be seen in patterns for children's clothing; and even pictures of the flower are scarcely ever suspended in a room. The reason is that the lotos, being the symbolic flower of Buddhism, is sculptured upon tombstones, and is borne as an emblem in funeral processions.

also cake, and a *bii-bii* likewise, and a rattle as well, and an *okiagarikoboshi* that will stand up immediately after being thrown down.

(*Shidzuoka City.*)

Yoi-ko da !

San-ko da !

Mamé na ko da !

Mamé dé sodatéta

O-ko ja mono !

Néruto nérimochi

Kurétéyaru ;

Damaruto dango wo

Kurétéyaru ;

Nakuto nagamochi

Showaséru zō ;

Okoruto okorimushi ni

Kurétéyaru.

Good child, genteel child, — what a healthy child it is ! For it is a child that has been nourished with peas. — Kneaded rice-cakes I will give you if you sleep. Dumplings I will give you if you hush. If you cry I will make you carry a *nagamochi* [quilt-chest]. If you get angry I will give you to the Anger-Insect.[1]

---

[1] The chief interest of this composition is the curiously alliterative structure of the phrases. There are several queer plays upon words, *Mamé*, as pronounced, may mean either " peas " or " healthy." In the

(*Province of Suruga.*)

Bō ya wa iiko da !
Nennéshina !
Kono ko no kawaisa
Kagiri nai, —
Yama de no ki no kazu,
Kaya no kazu,
Ten é nobotté
Hoshi no kazu,
Numadzu é kudaréba
Senbon matsu, —
Senbon-matsubara,
Ko-matsubara,
Matsuba no kazu yori
Mada kawai !

Oh ! how good a child this boy is ! Sleep, my child ! —
My love of this child is incàlculable as the number of the
trees in the mountain-forest, — as the number of the fruits
of the *kaya*, — as the number of the stars in the sky above,
— as the thousands of the pines of Numadzu below, — as
the myriad great pines of the pine-forest, — as the myriad
little pines of the young pine-wood : more incalculable even
than the leaves of those pine-trees, is my love of this little
one !

same way " okori " might mean either " to be angry " or " ague."
Okorimushi properly signifies the " ague-insect," and is the popular
name of a large moth, believed to cause chills and fever.

(Lullaby sung to the child of a Daimyō. — Province of Izumo.) [1]

O-nenné, o-nenné, o-nenné ya!

Yoi ni wa tōkara gyōshin nari.

Asama wa tōkara omézamété,

Omézamé no ohōbi ni nani, nani?

O-chichi no débana wo agémashozo,

O-chichi no débana ga o-iya nara,

Niwatori-kéawasé o-mé ni kakyō;

Niwatori-kéawasé o-iya nara,

O-kwashi wa takusan o-agarika!

Augustly rest, augustly rest! Soon this evening augustly sleep! Early at daybreak, at the august awakening, what, what honorable gift shall be presented at the august awakening? Flower of honorable milk shall be presented. If the flower of honorable milk be augustly disliked, then the fighting of the cocks will be honorably displayed. If the fighting of the cocks be augustly disliked, then will not honorable cake be augustly accepted?

(Tōkyō.)

Nennen yō!

Korokoro yō!

Nennen-Koyama no

Usagi wa,

---

[1] Obtained from dictation at Matsuë, Izumo. The original interest of this piece lies in the curious and really untranslatable honorifics.

Nazé ni o-mimi ga
O-nagai né ?
Okkasan no
O-naka ni,
Ita toki ni,
Biwa no mi,
Sasa no mi,
Tabémashité ; —
Soré dé o-mimi ga
O-nagai yo ! [1]

Sleep, little one ! — pleasantly sleep ! — Why are the ears
of the hare of the Hill of Nennen so honorably long ?
When he was in his mother's honorable womb, she ate the
fruits of the loquat, the seeds of the small bamboo : therefore his honorable ears are thus honorably long !

(*Province of Settsu.*)

Nenné ! Koro ïchi ! —
Temma no ichi yo !
Daikon soroëté,
Funé ni tsumu.
Funé ni tsundara

---

[1] An Izumo version of this lullaby will be found in *Glimpses of Unfamiliar Japan*, — p. 609. The Izumo version is more interesting. —
There are several Tōkyō versions.

Doko-madé ikiyaru ?
Kizu ya Namba no
Hashi no shita.
Hashi no shita ni wa
O-kamé ga iyaru ;
O-kamé toritaya,
Také hoshiya !
Také ga hoshikérya,
Takéya é ikiyaré ;
Také wa nandémo
Gozarimasu !

Sleep, child ! Fair-time is coming. Oh ! the fair of
Temma ! — The ends of the radishes having been evenly
trimmed, the ship is loaded. Having been laden, where
will the ship go ? — Under the Bridge of Kizu, and under the
Bridge of Namba. — Under those bridges live many honorable tortoises. Honorable tortoises I want to catch ! —
I want a bamboo-pole. — If you wish for a bamboo-pole,
go to the bamboo-shop. In that bamboo-shop all kinds of
bamboos augustly exist.

(*Tōkyō.*)

O-Tsuki Sama, ikutsu ?
Jiu-san, nanatsu.
Mada toshi waka yé !
Ano ko wo undé,
Kono ko wo undé,

Daré ni dakashō?
O-Man ni dakashō.
O-Man doko itta?
Abura-kaë, cha-kaë.
Aburaya no maë dë
Subité korondé;
Abura isshō koboshita.
Sono abura doshita?
Tarō-Don no inu to,
Jirō-Don no inu to,
Mina namété shimatta.
Sono inu doshita?
Taiko ni hatté,
Achi no hō démo,
Don-doko-don!
Kochi no hō démo,
Don-doko-don!
Tataita-to-sa!

Lady Moon, how old are you? — Thirteen, seven. —
That is still young. — That child being born, this child be-
ing born, to whom shall the child be given to carry? — To
O-Man it shall be given to carry. — Where is O-Man gone?
— She has gone to buy oil; she has gone to buy tea. —
Slipping and falling, in front of the oil-shop, one whole
shō[1] of oil she spilled. — What was done with that oil? —

---

[1] One shō is a little more than a quart and a half.

The dog of Master Tarō, and the dog of Master Jirō, licked it all up. — What was done with those dogs? — Their skins were stretched and made into drums. There you can hear [*the drum*] even now, — *don-doko-don!* Here you can hear [*the drum*] even now, — *don-doko-don !* So they beat the drums !

(*Province of Gifu.*)

Nenné ya ! korokoro ya !
Nenné no umaréta
Sono hi ni wa,
Akai o-mamma ni
Toto soëté,
Toto-sama no o-hashi dé
Agémashōka ?
Toto-sama no o-hashi wa
Toto kusai.
Haha-sama no o-hashi dé
Agémashōka ?
Haha-sama no o-hashi wa
Chichi kusai.
Ané-sama no o-hashi dé
Agémashō.
Nennen ! korokoro
Nenné-shō !

Sleep, little one ! happily sleep ! On your next birthday I will give you red rice cooked with fish. Shall I then

feed you with the honorable chopsticks of your father?—
The honorable chopsticks of father smell of fish.—Shall I
feed you with the honorable chopsticks of your mother?—
Mother's honorable chopsticks smell of milk.—Then I
shall feed you with the honorable chopsticks of your elder
sister.—Sleep! pleasantly go to sleep!

(Province of Settsu.)

Nennéko, sannéko, sakaya no ko!
Sakaya wo iyanara yomé ni yarō.
Yomé no dōgu wa, nani-nani zo?
Tansu, nagamochi, hitsu, todana;
Ryūkyū-zutsumi ga rokka aru;
Furoshiki-zutsumi wa kazu shirézu
Soréhodo koshiraë yaru-kara-nya;
Isshō sararété modoruna yo!
— Sorya mata okkasan dōyoku na!
Sengoku tsundaru funé saëmo,
Kazé ga kawaréba modoru mono!

Sleep, sleep, my child,—child of the *saké*-dealer! If
you do not like this *saké*-house, I will send you away as a
bride. What are the bridal-gifts that will be given? A
tansu (chest of drawers), a *nagamochi* (quilt-chest), one
hitsu (clothes-chest), one *todana* (cupboard). Of Ryūkyū [1]
goods the packages are six;—as for the presents wrapped

---

[1] *Ryūkyū* is the Japanese name of the Loochoo Islands. Various
textile and other fabrics, made in the Loochoo islands, are greatly
prized in Japan.

in *furoshiki*,[1] their number cannot be told. So much having been done for you, when you are given as a bride, remember that if you be divorced, you must never in your life come back to this house! — Ah, mother! that is too cruel of you! Even the ship that is freighted with a thousand *koku* of rice returns to port if the fair wind changes.

(*Tōkyō Lullaby*.)

Senjō zashiki no
Karakami sodachi!
Botchama mo yoi ko ni
Naru toki wa,
Jimen wo fuyashité,
Kura tatété,
Kura no tonari ni
Matsu uëté,
Matsu no tonari ni
Také uëté,
Také no tonari ni
Umé uëté,
Umé no ko-éda ni
Suzu sagété, —
Sono suzu chara-chara
Naru toki wa,

---

[1] Small presents are usually wrapped in a square piece of cotton or silk before being sent; and this wrapper, much resembling a large handkerchief, is called a *furoshiki*.

Botchama mo sazo-sazo
Uréshikarō!

[Big and beautiful] as the sliding-screens of a thousand-mat room, — so Sir Baby-boy is growing! When he becomes a good boy likewise, then I will make larger the grounds about our dwelling, and there build for him a treasure-house. Next to the treasure-house I will plant pine-trees. Next to the pine-trees I will plant bamboos. Next to the bamboos I will plant plum-trees. To the little branches of those plum-trees shall be hung little bells. When those little bells sound *chara-chara* — O Sir Baby-boy, how happy you will be!

(*City of Hakata.*)

Kinkan, mikan, nambō tabéta?
O-tera no nikai dé mitsu tabéta.
Sono o-tera wa daré ga tatéta?
Hachiman-Chōja no oto-musumé.
Oto ga yomé-iri suru toki nya
Nangai-teramachi shara-shara to,
Mijikai-teramachi shara-shara to.
Shara-shara setta no o ga kiréta:
— Anésan, tatété kurénkana?
— Tatété yarō kota yarokendo
Hari mo nakaréba, ito mo nai.
— Hari wa hariya dé kōté-yaru,
Ito wa itoya dé kōté-yaru.

— Hari wa hariya no kusaré-bari,
Ito wa itoya no kusaré-ito !
— Anésan, setta ni chi ga tsuita !
— Soré wa chi ja nai — béni ja mono !
Ōsaka béni koso iro yokéré ;
Iro no yoi hodo né ga takai.

— Citrons, oranges, — how many did you eat ?
— Upstairs in the honorable temple I ate three.
— As for that honorable temple, — by whom was it built ?
By the youngest daughter of the wealthy Hachiman.
On the day when that youngest daughter went out to be married,
Down the long Street-of-Temples she walked — *shara-shara,*
Down the short Street-of-Temples she walked — *shara-shara:*
Then was broken a thong of the sandals [1] that sounded *shara-shara.*
" Elder sister, will you not kindly mend it ? "
" The thong I would mend for you ;
But I have neither a needle nor thread."
" A needle from the needle-shop I will buy for you ;
Thread from the threadshop I will buy for you."
" Ah, this needle of the needle-shop is a rotten needle !
This thread of the thread-shop is rotten thread."
" Elder Sister ! there is blood upon my sandals ! "

---

[1] The *setta* is a light, but very strong sandal, of which the leather sole is strengthened with plates of thin metal.

" That is not blood, it is only *béni* (rouge).[1]
The rouge of Osaka has indeed a fine color:
Very fine is the color, — therefore the price is dear."

.   .   .   .   .   .

And now, by way of conclusion, let me state
that in preparing this rather lengthy paper I could
only hope to furnish the reader with a new
experience, — an experience somewhat like that
of passing, for the first time, through Japanese
streets.

The first general impression of a Japanese
street must be, for most people, even more
vague than strange.   Unless you happen to
have senses of superlative delicacy, — unless you
possess a visual faculty like that of Pierre Loti,
for example, — you can remember very little,
and understand almost nothing, of what you
looked at while passing through that street.
Nevertheless you will find yourself surprised and
pleased; — you will feel, without knowing why,
the sensation of the elfish and the odd, — the
charm of the unexpected.

Well, in all the child-songs which I have quoted,
perhaps less than half-a-dozen fairly arrested your
attention; and of the rest you probably remem-

---

[1] *Béni* is used chiefly to color the lips.

ber scarcely anything. But if you have read through the series, even hastily and superficially, you should have obtained a general impression, or vague sensation, not unlike the sensation that follows upon the first vision of Japanese streets: — dim surmise of another and inscrutable humanity, — another race-soul, strangely alluring, yet forever alien to your own.

STUDIES HERE AND THERE

On a Bridge

MY old kurumaya, Heishichi, was taking me to a famous temple in the neighborhood of Kumamoto.

We came to a humped and venerable bridge over the Shirakawa; and I told Heishichi to halt on the bridge, so that I could enjoy the view for a moment. Under the summer sky, and steeped in a flood of sunshine electrically white, the colors of the land seemed almost unreally beautiful. Below us the shallow river laughed and gurgled over its bed of grey stones, overshadowed by verdure of a hundred tints. Before us the reddish-white road alternately vanished and re-appeared as it wound away, through grove or hamlet, toward the high blue ring of peaks encircling the vast Plain of Higo. Behind us lay Kumamoto, — a far bluish confusion of myriad roofs; — only the fine grey lines of its castle showing sharp against the green of further wooded hills. . . . Seen from within, Kumamoto is a shabby place; but seen as I beheld it that summer day, it is a fairy-city, built out of mist and dreams. . . .

"Twenty-two years ago," said Heishichi, wiping his forehead — "no, twenty-three years ago, — I stood here, and saw the city burn."

"At night?" I queried.

"No," said the old man, "it was in the afternoon — a wet day. . . . They were fighting; and the city was on fire."

"Who were fighting?"

"The soldiers in the castle were fighting with the Satsuma men. We dug holes in the ground and sat in them, to escape the balls. The Satsuma men had cannons on the hill; and the soldiers in the castle were shooting at them over our heads. The whole city was burned."

"But how did you happen to be here?"

"I ran away. I ran as far as this bridge, — all by myself. I thought that I could get to my brother's farm — about seven miles from here. But they stopped me."

"Who stopped you?"

"Satsuma men, — I don't know who they were. As I got to the bridge I saw three peasants — I thought they were peasants — leaning over the railing: men wearing big straw hats and straw rain-cloaks and straw sandals. I spoke to them politely; and one of them turned his head round, and said to me, 'You stay here!' That was all he said: the others did not say anything. Then I saw that they were not peasants; and I was afraid."

"How did you know that they were not peasants?"

"They had long swords hidden under their rain-cloaks, — very long swords. They were very tall men. They leaned over the bridge, looking down into the river. I stood beside them, — just there, by the third post to the left, and did as they did. I knew that they would kill me if I moved from there. None of them spoke. And we four stood leaning over the railing for a long time."

"How long?"

"I do not know exactly — it must have been a long time. I saw the city burning. All that while none of the men spoke to me or looked at me: they kept their eyes upon the water. Then I heard a horse; and I saw a cavalry officer coming at a trot, — looking all about him as he came. . . ."

" From the city ? "

" Yes, — along that road behind you. . . . The
three men watched him from under their big
straw hats ; but they did not turn their heads ; —
they pretended to be looking down into the river.
But, the moment that the horse got on the bridge,
the three men turned and leaped ; — and one
caught the horse's bridle ; and another gripped the
officer's arm ; and the third cut off his head — all
in a moment. . . ."

" The officer's head ? "

" Yes — he did not even have time to shout
before his head was off. . . . I never saw anything done so quickly. Not one of the three
men uttered a word."

" And then ? "

" Then they pitched the body over the railing
into the river ; and one of them struck the horse,
— hard ; and the horse ran away. . . ."

" Back to the town ? "

" No — the horse was driven straight out over
the bridge, into the country. . . . The head was
not thrown into the river : one of the Satsuma
men kept it — under his straw cloak. . . . Then
all of us leaned over the railing, as before, —
looking down. My knees were shaking. The

three samurai did not speak a single word. I
could not even hear them breathing. I was
afraid to look at their faces; — I kept looking
down into the river. . . . After a little while I
heard another horse, — and my heart jumped so
that I felt sick; — and I looked up, and saw a
cavalry-soldier coming along the road, riding very
fast. No one stirred till he was on the bridge:
then — in one second — his head was off! The
body was thrown into the river, and the horse
driven away — exactly as before. Three men
were killed like that. Then the samurai left the
bridge."

"Did you go with them?"

"No: they left immediately after having
killed the third man, — taking the heads with
them; — and they paid no attention to me. I
stayed on the bridge, afraid to move, until they
were very far away. Then I ran back to the
burning town; — I ran quick, quick! There I
was told that the Satsuma troops were retreating.
Soon afterwards, the army came from Tōkyō;
and I was given some work: I carried straw sandals for the soldiers."

"Who were the men that you saw killed on
the bridge?"

" I don't know."

" Did you never try to find out ? "

" No," said Heishichi, again mopping his fore-head : " I said nothing about the matter until many years after the war."

" But why ? " I persisted.

Heishichi gave me one astonished look, smiled in a pitying way, and answered, —

" Because it would have been wrong; — it would have been ungrateful."

I felt properly rebuked.

And we resumed our journey.

The Case of O-Dai

I

O—DAI pushed aside the lamplet and the incense-cup and the water vessel on the Buddha-shelf, and opened the little shrine before which they had been placed. Within were the *ihai,* the mortuary tablets of her people, —five in all; and a gilded figure of the Bōdhisattva Kwannon stood smiling behind them. The *ihai* of the grandparents occupied the left side; those of the parents the right; and between them was a smaller tablet, bearing the *kaimyo* of a child-brother with whom she used to play and quarrel, to laugh and cry, in other and happier years. Also the shrine contained a *makémono,* or scroll, inscribed with the spirit-names of many ancestors. Before that shrine, from her infancy, O-Dai had been wont to pray.

231

The tablets and the scroll signified more to
her faith in former time — very much more —
than remembrance of a father's affection and a
mother's caress; — more than any remembrance
of the ever-loving, ever-patient, ever-smiling
elders who had fostered her babyhood, carried
her pickaback to every temple-festival, invented
her pleasures, consoled her small sorrows, and
soothed her fretfulness with song; — more than
the memory of the laughter and the tears, the
cooing and the calling and the running of the
dear and mischievous little brother; — more than
all the traditions of the ancestors.

For those objects signified the actual viewless
presence of the lost, — the haunting of invisible
sympathy and tenderness, — the gladness and
the grief of the dead in the joy and the sorrow
of the living. When, in other time, at evening
dusk, she was wont to kindle the lamplet before
them, how often had she seen the tiny flame
astir with a motion not its own!

Yet the *ihai* is even more than a token to
pious fancy. Strange possibilities of transmuta-
tion, transubstantiation, belong to it. It serves
as temporary body for the spirit between death

and birth: each fibre of its incense-penetrated wood lives with a viewless life-potential. The will of the ghost may quicken it. Sometimes, through power of love, it changes to flesh and blood. By help of the *ihai* the buried mother returns to suckle her babe in the dark. By help of the *ihai,* the maid consumed upon the funeral pyre may return to wed her betrothed, — even to bless him with a son. By power of the *ihai,* the dead servant may come back from the dust of his rest to save his lord from ruin. Then, after love or loyalty has wrought its will, the personality vanishes ; — the body again becomes, to outward seeming, only a tablet.

All this O-Dai ought to have known and re-membered. Maybe she did ; for she wept as she took the tablets and the scroll out of the shrine, and dropped them from a window into the river below. She did not dare to look after them, as the current whirled them away.

II

O-DAI had done this by order of two English missionary-women who, by various acts of seeming kindness, had persuaded her to become a Christian. (Converts are always commanded to bury or to cast away their ancestral tablets.) These missionary-women — the first ever seen in the province — had promised O-Dai, their only convert, an allowance of three *yen* a month, as assistant, — because she could read and write. By the toil of her hands she had never been able to earn more than two yen a month; and out of that sum she had to pay a rent of twenty-five *sen* for the use of the upper floor of a little house, belonging to a dealer in second-hand goods. Thither, after the death of her parents, she had taken her loom, and the ancestral tablets. She had been obliged to work very hard indeed in order to live. But with three *yen* a month she could live very well; and the missionary-women had a room for her. She did not think that the people would mind her change of religion.

As a matter of fact they did not much care. They did not know anything about Christianity, and did not want to know: they only laughed at the girl for being so foolish as to follow the ways of the foreign women. They regarded her as a dupe, and mocked her without malice.

And they continued to laugh at her, good-humoredly enough, until the day when she was seen to throw the tablets into the river. Then they stopped laughing. They judged the act in itself, without discussing its motives. Their judgment was instantaneous, unanimous, and voiceless. They said no word of reproach to O-Dai. They merely ignored her existence.

The moral resentment of a Japanese community is not always a hot resentment, — not the kind that quickly burns itself out. It may be cold. In the case of O-Dai it was cold and silent and heavy like a thickening of ice. No one uttered it. It was altogether spontaneous, instinctive. But the universal feeling might have been thus translated into speech: —

"Human society, in this most eastern East, has been held together from immemorial time by virtue of that cult which exacts the gratitude of the present to the past, the reverence of the living for the dead, the affection of the descendant for the ancestor. Far beyond the visible world extends the duty of the child to the parent, of the servant to the master, of the subject to the sovereign. Therefore do the dead preside in the family council, in the communal assembly, in the high seats of judgment, in the governing of cities, in the ruling of the land.

" Against the Virtue Supreme of Filial Piety, — against the religion of the Ancestors, — against all faith and gratitude and reverence and duty, — against the total moral experience of her race, — O-Dai has sinned the sin that cannot be forgiven. Therefore shall the people account her a creature impure, — less deserving of fellowship than the Éta, — less worthy of kindness than the dog in the street or the cat upon the roof; since even these, according to their feebler light, observe the common law of duty and affection.

"O-Dai has refused to her dead the word of thankfulness, the whisper of love, the reverence of a daughter. Therefore, now and forever, the living shall refuse to her the word of greeting, the common salutation, the kindly answer.

" O-Dai has mocked the memory of the father who begot her, the memory of the mother whose breasts she sucked, the memory of the elders who cherished her childhood, the memory of the little one who called her Sister. She has mocked at love: therefore all love shall be denied her, all offices of affection.

"To the spirit of the father who begot her, to the spirit of the mother who bore her, O-Dai has refused the shadow of a roof, and the vapor of food, and the offering of water. Even so to her shall be denied the shelter of a roof, and the gift of food, and the cup of refreshment.

"And even as she cast out the dead, the living shall cast her out. As a carcass shall she be in the way, — as the small carrion that none will turn to look upon, that none will bury, that none will pity, that none will speak for in prayer to the Gods and the Buddhas. As a *Gaki*[1] she shall be, — as a *Shōjiki-Gaki,* — seeking sustenance in refuse-heaps. Alive into hell shall she enter; — yet shall her hell remain the single hell, the solitary hell, the hell *Kodoku,* that spheres the spirit accurst in solitude of fire. . . ."

III

UNEXPECTEDLY the missionary-women informed O-Dai that she would have to take care of herself. Perhaps she had done her best; but

[1] Prêta.

she certainly had not been to them of any use
whatever, and they required a capable assistant.
Moreover they were going away for some time,
and could not take her with them. Surely she
could not have been so foolish as to think that
they were going to give her three yen per month
merely for being a Christian! . . .

O-Dai cried; and they advised her to be
brave, and to walk in the paths of virtue. She
said that she could not find employment: they
told her that no industrious and honest person
need ever want for work in this busy world.
Then, in desperate terror, she told them truths
which they could not understand, and energeti-
cally refused to believe. She spoke of a danger
imminent; and they answered her with all the
harshness of which they were capable, — believ-
ing that she had confessed herself utterly de-
praved. In this they were wrong. There was
no atom of vice in the girl: an amiable weak-
ness and a childish trustfulness were the worst
of her faults. Really she needed help, — needed
it quickly, — needed it terribly. But they could
understand only that she wanted money; and
that she had threatened to commit sin if she
did not get it. They owed her nothing, as she

had always been paid in advance; and they imagined excellent reasons for denying her further aid
of any sort.

So they put her into the street. Already she
had sold her loom. She had nothing more to
sell except the single robe upon her back, and
a few pair of useless *tabi,* or cleft stockings,
which the missionary-women had obliged her
to buy, because they thought that it was im-
modest for a young girl to be seen with naked
feet. (They had also obliged her to twist her
hair into a hideous back-knot, because the Japanese style of wearing the hair seemed to them
ungodly.)

What becomes of the Japanese girl publicly
convicted of offending against filial piety? What
becomes of the English girl publicly convicted
of unchastity? . . .

Of course, had she been strong, O-Dai might
have filled her sleeves with stones, and thrown
herself into the river, — which would have been
an excellent thing to do under the circumstances.
Or she might have cut her throat, — which is
more respectable, as the act requires both nerve
and skill. But, like most converts of her class,

O-Dai was weak: the courage of the race had failed in her. She wanted still to see the sun; and she was not of the sturdy type able to wrestle with the earth for that privilege. Even after fully abjuring her errors, there was left. but one road for her to travel.

Said the person who bought the body of O-Dai at a third of the price prayed for: —

"My business is an exceedingly shameful business. But even into this business no woman can be received who is known to have done the thing that you have done. If I were to take you into my house, no visitors would come; and the people would probably make trouble. Therefore to Ōsaka, where you are not known, you shall be sent; and the house in Ōsaka will pay the money. . . ."

So vanished forever O-Dai, — flung into the furnace of a city's lust. . . . Perhaps she existed only to furnish one example of facts that every foreign missionary ought to try to understand.

Beside the Sea

I

THE Buddhist priests had announced that a *Ségaki*-service, in behalf of all the drowned folk of Yaidzu, would be held on the shore at two o'clock in the afternoon. Yaidzu is an ancient place — (it is mentioned, under the name of "Yakidzu," in the oldest chronicles of Japan) ; — and for thousands of years the fishers of Yaidzu have been regularly paying their toll of life to the great deep. And the announcement of the priests reminded me of something very much older than Buddhism, — the fancy that the spirits of the drowned move with the waters forever. According to this belief, the sea off Yaidzu must be thick with souls. . . .

Early in the afternoon I went to the shore to observe preparations; and I found a multitude of people already there assembled. It was a burn-

ing July day — not a speck of cloud visible; and
the coarse shingle of the slope, under the blaze of
sun, was radiating heat like slag just raked from
a furnace.   But those fisher-folk, tanned to all
tints of bronze, did not mind the sun: they sat
on the scorching stones, and waited.   The sea
was at ebb, and gentle, — moving in slow, long,
lazy ripples.

Upon the beach there had been erected a kind
of rude altar, about four feet high; and on this
had been placed an immense *ibai,* or mortuary
tablet, of unpainted wood, — the back of the tablet being turned to the sea.   The *ibai* bore, in
large Chinese characters, the inscription, *Sangai-
Ban-Rei-I,* — signifying, " Resting-place [or, *seat*]
of the myriad [*innumerable*] spirits of the Three
States of Existence."   Various food-offerings had
been set before this tablet, — including a bowl of
cooked rice; rice-cakes; eggplants; pears; and,
piled upon a fresh lotos leaf, a quantity of what
is called *hyaku-mi-no-onjiki*.   It is really a mixture of rice and sliced eggplant, though the name
implies one hundred different kinds of nourish-
ment.   In the bowl of boiled rice tiny sticks were
fixed, with cuttings of colored paper attached to

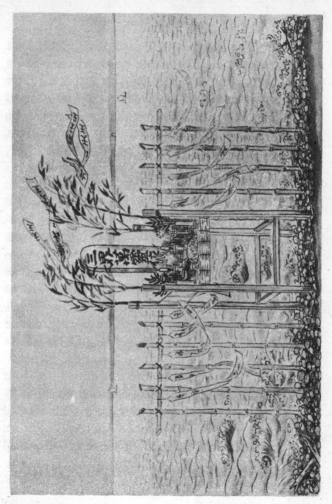

The Feast of the Ghosts

them. I also observed candles, a censer, some
bundles of incense-rods, a vessel of water, and a
pair of bamboo cups containing sprays of the
sacred plant *shikimi*.[1]   Beside the water-vessel
there had been laid a bunch of *misohagi*,[2] with
which to sprinkle water upon the food-offerings,
according to the prescriptions of the rite.

To each of the four posts supporting the altar
a freshly-cut bamboo had been attached; and
other bamboos had been planted in the beach, to
right and left of the structure; and to every bamboo was fastened a little banner inscribed with
Chinese characters.   The banners of the bamboos·
at the four corners of the altar bore the names
and attributes of the Four Deva Kings, — Zōchō
Tennō, guardian of the West; Jikoku Tennō,
guardian of the East; Tamon Tennō, guardian of
the North; and Kōmoku Tennō, guardian of the
South.

In front of the altar straw-mattings had been
laid, so as to cover a space of beach about thirty
feet long by fifteen wide ; and above this matted
space awnings of blue cotton had been rigged up,
to shelter the priests from the sun.   I squatted

---

[1] *Illicium religiosum.*

[2] A kind of bush-clover.

down awhile under the awnings to make a rough drawing (afterwards corrected and elaborated by a Japanese friend) of the altar and the offerings.

The service was not held at the appointed time: it must have been nearly three o'clock when the priests made their appearance. There were seven of them, in vestments of great ceremony; and they were accompanied by acolytes carrying bells, books, stools, reading-stands, and other necessary furniture. Priests and acolytes took their places under the blue awning; the spectators standing outside, in the sun. Only one of the priests, — the chief officiant, — sat facing the altar; the others, with their acolytes, seated themselves to right and left of him, — so as to form two ranks, facing each other.

II

AFTER some preliminary rearrangement of the offerings upon the altar, and the kindling of some incense-rods, the ceremony proper began with a Buddhist hymn, or gâthâ, which was chanted to the accompaniment of *hyōshigi*[1] and of bells.

---

[1] *Hyōshigi* are small blocks of hard wood, which are used, either for signalling or for musical purposes, by strik-

There were two bells,—a large deep-sounding
bell; and a small bell of very sweet tone,—in
charge of a little boy. The big bell was tapped
slowly; the little bell was sounded rapidly; and
the *hyōshigi* rattled almost like a pair of castanets.
And the effect of the gâthâ as chanted by all
the officiants in unison, with this extraordinary
instrumentation, was not less impressive than
strange:—

> *Biku Bikuni*
> *Hosshin hōji*
> *Ikki jō-jiki,*
> *Fusé jippō,*
> *Kyū-jin kokū,*
> *Shūhen hōkai,*
> *Mijin setchū*
> *Sho-u kokudo,*
> *Issai gaki;*
> *Senbō kyūmétsu,*
> *Sansen chishu,*
> *Naishi koya,*
> *Shō-kijin to,*
> *Shōrai shushi. . . .*

---

ing them quickly together so as to produce a succession of
sharp dry sounds.

This brief sonorous metre seemed to me particularly well adapted for invocatory or incantatory chanting; and the gâthâ of the *ségaki*-service was indeed a veritable incantation, — as the following free translation will make manifest : —

"We, Bhikshus and Bhikunis, devoutly presenting this vessel of pure food, do offer the same to all, without exception, of the Pretas dwelling in the Ten Directions of Space, in the surrounding Dharma-worlds, and in every part of the Earth, — not excepting the smallest atom of dust within a temple. And also to the spirits of those long dead and passed away, — and likewise unto the Lord-Spirits of mountain and river and soil, and of waste places. — Hither deign therefore to approach and to gather, all ye goblins ! — we now, out of our pity and compassion, desire to give you food. We wish that each and all of you may enjoy this our food-gift. And moreover we shall pray, doing homage to all the Buddhas and to all the Heavenly Ones who dwell within the Zones of Formlessness, that you, and that all beings having desire, may be enabled to obtain contentment. We shall pray that all of you, by virtue of the utterance of the dhâranîs, and by the enjoyment of this food-offering, may find the higher knowledge, and be freed from every pain, and soon obtain rebirth in the Zone Celestial, — there to know every bliss, moving freely in all the Ten Directions, and finding everywhere delight. — Awaken within yourselves the Bodhi-Mind ! — follow the Way of Enlightenment ! Rise to Buddhahood ! Turn ye no more backward ! — neither linger on the path ! Let such among you as first obtain the Way vow each to lead up the rest, and so become free ! — Also we beseech you now to watch

over us and to guard us, by night ánd by dąy.　Ańd help us
even now to obtain our desire in bestowing this food upon
you,—that the merit produced by this ąction may be
extended to all beings dwelling within the Dharma-worlds,
and that the power of this merit may help to spread the
Truth through all those Dharma-worlds, and help all beings
therein to find the Supreme Enlightenment, and to obtain
all wisdom.— And we now pray that all your acts hereafter
may serve to gain for you the merit that will help you to
Buddhahood.　And thus we desire that you quickly become
Buddhas."

Then began the most curious part of the service, — namely, the sprinkling and the presenta-
tion of the food-offerings, with recitation of
certain dhâranîs, or magical verses, composed of
talismanic Sanscrit words.　This portion of the
rite was brief; but to recount all its details would
require much space, — every utterance or gesture
of the officiant being made according to rule.
For example, the hands and fingers of the priest,
during the recital of any dhâranî, must be held in
a position prescribed for that particular dhâranî.
But the principal incidents of this complicated
ritual are about as follows:

First of all is recited, seven times, the Dhâranî
of Invitation, to summon the spirits from the Ten
Directions of Space.　During its recitation the
officiant must hold out his right hand, with

the tip of the middle finger touching the tip of
the thumb, and the rest of the fingers extended.
Then is recited, with a different, but equally
weird gesture, the Dhâranî of the Breaking
of the Gates of Hell. Next is repeated the
Se-Kanrō verse, or Dhâranî of the Bestowal of
the Amrita, — by virtue of which it is supposed
that the food-offerings are transformed, for the
sake of the ghosts, into heavenly nectar and am-
brosia. And thereafter is chanted, three times,
an invocation to the Five Tathâgatas: —

"Salutation to Hōshō Nyōrai, — hereby besought to
relieve [*the Pretas*] from the karma of all desire, and to fill
them with bliss !

"Salutation to Myō-Shikishin-Nyōrai, — besought to
take away from them every imperfection of form !

"Salutation to Kanrō-Ō-Nyōrai, — besought to purify
their bodies and their minds, and to give them peace of
heart !

"Salutation to Kobaku-Shin-Nyōrai, — besought to
favor them with the delight of excellent taste !

"Salutation to Rifui-Nyōrai, — besought to free them
from all their fears, and to deliver them out of the World
of Hungry Spirits ! "

The book *Bongyō Ségaki-Monben* says: —

"When the officiants have thus recited the
names of the Five Tathâgatas, then, by the grace of
the power of those Buddhas, all the Pretas shall be

liberated from the karma of their former errors, — shall experience immeasurable bliss, — shall receive excellent features and complete bodies, — shall be rid of all their terrors, — and, after having partaken of the food-offerings which have been changed for them into amrita of delightful taste, shall soon be reborn into the Pure Land [*Jōdo*]."

After the invocation of the Five Tathâgatas, other verses are recited; and during this recitation the food-offerings are removed, one by one. (There is a mysterious regulation that, after having been taken from the altar, they must not be placed under a willow-tree, a peach-tree, or a pomegranate-tree.) Last of all is recited the Dhârani of Dismissal, seven times, — the priest each time snapping his fingers as a signal to the ghosts that they are free to return. This is called the *Hakken,* or Sending-Away.

III

THE sea never ebbs far on this steep coast, — though it often rises tremendously, breaking into the town; and its gentler moods are not to be trusted. By way of precaution the posts of the *ihai*-stand had been driven deeply into the beach. The event proved that this precaution had not been taken in vain; for the rite began, owing to the delay of the priests, only with the turn of the tide. Even while the gâthâ was being chanted, the sea roughened and darkened; and then, — as if the outer deep responded, — the thunder-roll of a great breaker suddenly smothered the voices of the singers and the clanging of the bells. Soon another heavy surge boomed along the shore, — then another; and during the reciting of the dhâranîs the service could be heard only in the intervals of wave-bursts, — while the foam sheeted up the slope, whirling and hissing even to within a few paces of the altar. . . .

And again I found myself thinking of the old belief in some dim relation between the dead and the sea. In that moment the primitive fancy appeared to me much more reasonable and more humane than the ghastly doctrine of a Preta-world, with its thirty-six orders of hideous misery, — its swarms of goblins hungering and burning! . . . Nay, the poor dead! — why should they be thus deformed and doomed by human judgment?

Wiser and kindlier to dream of them as mingling
with flood and wind and cloud, — or quickening
the heart of the flower, — or flushing the cheek
of the fruit, — or shrilling with the cicadæ in
forest-solitudes, — or thinly humming in summer-
dusk with the gathering of the gnats. . . . I do
not believe, — I do not wish to believe in hungry
ghosts. . . . . Ghosts break up, I suppose, into
soul-dust at the touch of death, — though their
atoms, doubtless, thereafter recombine with other
dust for the making of other ghosts. . . . Still,
I cannot convince myself that even the grosser
substance of vanished being ever completely dies,
however dissolved or scattered, — fleeting in the
gale, — floating in the mists, — shuddering in the
leaf, — flickering in the light of waters, — or
tossed on some desolate coast in a thunder
of surf, to whiten and writhe in the clatter of
shingle. . . .

As the ceremony ended, a fisherman mounted
lightly to the top of one of the awning-posts;
and there, gymnastically poised, he began to
shower down upon the crowd a quantity of very
small rice-cakes, which the young folks scrambled
for, with shouts of laughter. After the uncanny

solemnity of that rite, the outburst of merriment was almost startling; but I found it also very natural, and pleasant, and human. Meanwhile the seven priests departed in many-colored procession, — their acolytes trudging wearily behind them, under much weight of stands and stools and bells. Soon the assembly scattered, — all the rice-cakes having been distributed and appropriated; — then the altar, the awnings, the mattings were removed; — and in a surprisingly short time every trace of the strange ceremony had disappeared. . . . I looked about me; — I was alone upon the beach. . . . There was no sound but the sound of the returning tide: a muttering enormous, appalling, — as of some Life innominable, that had been at peace, awakened to immeasurable pain. . . .

Drifting

A TYPHOON was coming; and I sat on the sea-wall in a great wind to look at the breakers; and old Amano Jinsuké sat beside me. Southeast all was black-blue gloom, except the sea, which had a strange and tawny color. Enormous surges were already towering in. A hundred yards away they crumbled over with thunder and earthquake, and sent their foam leaping and sheeting up the slope, to spring at our faces. After each long crash, the sound of the shingle retreating was exactly like the roar of a railway train at full speed. I told Amano Jinsuké that it made me afraid; and he smiled.

"I swam for two nights and two days," he said, "in a sea worse than this. I was nineteen years old at the time. Out of a crew of eight, I was the only man saved.

255

"Our ship was called the *Fukuju Maru;*[1] — she was owned by Mayéda Jingorō, of this town. All of the crew but one were Yaidzu men. The captain was Saito Kichiyĕmon, — a man more than sixty years of age: he lived in Jō-no-Koshi, — the street just behind us. There was another old man on board, called Nito Shōshichi, who lived in the Araya quarter. Then there was Terao Kankichi, forty-two years old: his brother Minosuké, a lad of sixteen, was also with us. The Terao folk lived in Araya. Then there was Saito Heikichi, thirty years old; and there was a man called Matsushirō; — he came from Suō, but had settled in Yaidzu. Washino Otokichi was another of the crew: he lived in Jō-no-Koshi, and was only twenty-one. I was the youngest on board, — excepting Terao Minosuké.

"We sailed from Yaidzu on the morning of the tenth day of the seventh month of Manyen Gwannen,[2] — the Year of the Ape, — bound for Sanuki. On the night of the eleventh, in the

---

[1] The word *Fukuju* signifies "Fortunate Longevity."

[2] That is to say the first, or coronation-year, of the Period Manyen, — 1860–1861.

Kishū offing, we were caught by a typhoon from the southeast. A little before midnight, the ship capsized. As I felt her going over, I caught a plank, and threw it out, and jumped. It was blowing fearfully at the time; and the night was so dark that I could see only a few feet away; but I was lucky enough to find that plank, and put it under me. In another moment the ship was gone. Near me in the water were Washino Otokichi and the Terao‚ brothers and the man Matsushirō, — all swimming. There was no sign of the rest: they probably went down with the ship. We five kept calling to each other as we went up and down with the great seas; and I found that every one except Terao Kankichi had a plank or a timber of some sort. I cried to Kankichi: — 'Elder brother, you have children, and I am very young; — let me give you this plank!' He shouted back: — 'In this sea a plank is dangerous! — keep away from timber, Jinyō! — you may get hurt!' Before I could answer him, a wave like a black mountain burst over us. I was a long time under; and when I came up again, there was no sign of Kankichi. The younger men were still swimming; but they had been swept away to the

left of me; — I could not see them: we shouted
to each other. I tried to keep with the waves
— the others called to me: — ' Jinyō! Jinyō! —
come this way, — this way!' But I knew that
to go in their direction would be very dangerous; for every time that a wave struck me
sideways, I was taken under. So I called back
to them, 'Keep with the tide! — keep with the
current!' But they did not seem to understand;
— and they still called to me, *Kocchi é koi! —
kocchi é koi!* [1] — and their voices each time
sounded more and more far away. I became
afraid to answer. . . . The drowned call to you
like that when they want company: *Kocchi é
koi! — kocchi é koi!* . . .

"After a little time the calling ceased; and I
heard only the sea and the wind and the rain.
It was so dark that one could see the waves
only at the moment they went by, — high black
shadows, — each with a great pull. By the pull
of them I guessed how to direct myself. The
rain kept them from breaking much; — had it
not been for the rain, no man could have lived
long in such a sea. And hour after hour the

---

[1] " Come this way!"

wind became worse, and the swells grew higher;
— and I prayed for help to Jizō-Sama of Ogawa
all that night. . . . Lights? — yes, there were
lights in the water, but not many: the large
kind, that shine like candles. . . .

"At dawn the sea looked ugly, — a muddy
green; and the waves were like hills; and the
wind was terrible. Rain and spray made a fog
over the water; and there was no horizon. But
even if there had been land in sight I could have
done nothing except try to keep afloat. I felt
hungry, — very hungry; and the pain of the
hunger soon became hard to bear. All that day
I went up and down with the great waves, —
drifting under the wind and the rain; and there
was no sign of land. I did not know where I
was going: under that sky one could not tell
east from west.

"After dark the wind lulled; but the rain still
poured, and all was black. The pain of the
hunger passed; but I felt weak, — so weak that
I thought I must go under. Then I heard the
voices calling me, — just as they had called me
the night before: — 'Kocchi é koi! — kocchi é
koi!' . . . And, all at once, I saw the four men
of the *Fukuju Maru*, — not swimming, but

standing by me, — Terao Kankichi, and Terao Minosuké, and Washino Otokichi, and the man Matsushirō.   All looked at me with angry faces; and the boy Minosuké cried out, as in reproach: — 'Here I have to fix the helm; and you, Jinsuké, do nothing but sleep!'   Then Terao Kankichi — the one to whom I had offered the plank — bent over me with a *kakémono* in his hands, and half-unrolled it, and said: — 'Jinyō! here I have a picture of Amida Buddha — see! Now indeed you must repeat the *Nembutsu!*' He spoke strangely, in a way that made me afraid: I looked at the figure of the Buddha; and I repeated the prayer in great fear, — *Namu Amida Butsu! — namu Amida Butsu!*[1]   In the same moment a pain, like the pain of fire, stung through my thighs and hips; and I found that I had rolled off the plank into the sea.   The pain had been caused by a great *katsuo-no-éboshi.* . . . You never saw a *katsuo-no-éboshi?* It is a jelly-fish shaped like the *éboshi,* or cap, of a Shintō priest; and we call it the *katsuo-no-éboshi* because the katsuo-fish [bonito] feed upon

---

[1] This invocation, signifying " Salutation to the Buddha Amitâbha," is commonly repeated as a prayer for the dead.

it. When that thing appears anywhere, the
fishermen expect to catch many katsuo. The
body is clear like glass; but underneath there is
a kind of purple fringe, and long purple strings;
and when those strings touch you, the pain is
very great, and lasts for a long time. . . . That
pain revived me; if I had not been stung I might
never have awakened. I got on the plank again,
and prayed to Jizō-Sama of Ogawa, and to Kompira-Sama; and I was able to keep awake until
morning.

" Before daylight the rain stopped, and the sky
began to clear; for I could see some stars. At
dawn I got drowsy again; and I was awakened
by a blow on the head. A large sea-bird had
struck me. The sun was rising behind clouds;
and the waves had become gentle. Presently a
small brown bird flew by my face, — a coast-bird
(I do not know its real name); and I thought
that there must be land in sight. I looked behind
me, and I saw mountains. I did not recognize
the shapes of them: they were blue, — seemed to
be nine or ten *ri* distant. I made up my mind
to paddle towards them, — though I had little
hope of getting to shore. I was feeling hungry
again, — terribly hungry !

" I paddled towards the mountains, hour after hour. Once more I fell asleep; and once again a sea-bird struck me. All day I paddled. Towards evening I could tell, from the look of the mountains, that I was approaching them; but I knew that it would take me two days to reach the shore. I had almost ceased to hope when I caught sight of a ship, — a big junk. She was sailing towards me; but I saw that, unless I could swim faster, she would pass me at a great distance. It was my last chance: so I dropped the plank, and swam as fast as I could. I did get within about two chō of her: then I shouted. But I could see nobody on deck; and I got no answer. In another minute she had passed beyond me. The sun was setting; and I despaired. All of a sudden a man came on deck, and shouted to me: — 'Don't try to swim! don't tire yourself! — we are going to send a boat!' I saw the sail lowered at the same time; and I felt so glad that new strength seemed to come to me; — I swam on fast. Then the junk dropped a little boat; and as the boat came towards me, a man called out: — 'Is there anybody else? — have you dropped anything?' I answered: — 'I had nothing but a plank.' . . . In the same instant all my strength was gone : I felt the men in the boat pulling me up; but I could neither speak nor move, and everything became dark.

"After a time I heard the voices again, — the voices of the men of the *Fukuju Maru* : — ' Jinyō ! Jinyō ! ' — and I was frightened. Then somebody shook me, and said : — ' *Oi! oi!* [1] it is only a dream ! ' — and I saw that I was lying in the junk, under a hanging lantern (for it was night) ; — and beside me an old man, a stranger, was kneeling, with a cup of boiled rice in his hand. ' Try to eat a little,' he said, very kindly. I wanted to sit up, but could not : then he fed me himself, out of the cup. When it was empty I asked for more ; but the old man answered : — ' Not now ; — you must sleep first.' I heard him say to some one else : — ' Give him nothing more until I tell you : if you let him eat much, he will die.' I slept again ; and twice more that night I was given rice — soft-boiled rice — one small cupful at a time.

"In the morning I felt much better ; and the old man, who had brought me the rice, came and questioned me. When he heard about the loss of

---

[1] As we should say, "Hey ! hey ! " — to call attention.

our ship, and the time that I had been in the water, he expressed great pity for me. He told me that I had drifted, in those two nights and days, more than twenty-five *ri*.[1] 'We went after your plank,' he said, 'and picked it up. Perhaps you would like to present it some day to the temple of Kompira-Sama.' I thanked him, but answered that I wanted to offer it to the temple of Jizō-Sama of Ogawa, at Yaidzu; for it was to Jizō-Sama of Ogawa that I had most often prayed for help.

"The kind old man was the captain, and also the owner, of the junk. She was a Banshū ship, and was bound for the port of Kuki, in Kishū. . . . You write the name, *Ku-ki*, with the character for 'demon,' — so that it means the Nine Demons. . . . All the men of the ship were very good to me. I was naked, except for a loin-cloth, when I came on board; and they found clothes for me. One gave me an under-robe, and another an upper-robe, and another a girdle; — several gave me towels and sandals; — and all of them together made up a gift of money for me, amounting to between six and seven *ryō*.

---

[1] That is to say, about sixty-three English miles.

" When we reached Kuki — a nice little place, though it has a queer name — the captain took me to a good inn; and after a few days' rest I got strong again. Then the governor of the district, the Jitō, as we called him in those days, — sent for me, and heard my story, and had it written down. He told me that he would have to send a report of the matter to the Jitō of the Yaidzu district, after which he would find means to send me home. But the Banshū captain, who had saved me, offered to take me home in his own ship, and also to act as messenger for the Jitō; and there was much argument between the two. At that time we had no telegraph and no post; and to send a special messenger (*hikyaku*), from Kuki to Yaidzu,[1] would have cost at least fifty *ryō*. But, on the other hand, there were particular laws and customs about such matters, — laws very different from those of to-day. Meanwhile a Yaidzu ship came to the neighboring port of Arasha; and a woman of Kuki, who happened to be at Arasha, told the Yaidzu captain that I was at Kuki. The Yaidzu ship then came to Kuki; and the Jitō decided to send me home in

---

[1] The distance is more than one hundred and fifty miles.

charge of the Yaidzu captain, — giving him a
written order.

"Altogether, it was about a month from the
time of the loss of the *Fukuju Maru* when I returned to Yaidzu. We reached the harbor at
night; and I did not go home at once: it would
have frightened my people. Although no certain
news of the loss of our ship had then been received at Yaidzu, several things belonging to her
had been picked up by fishing-craft; and as the
typhoon had come very suddenly, with a terrible
sea, it was generally believed that the *Fukuju
Maru* had gone down, and that all of us had
been drowned. . . . None of the other men were
ever heard of again. . . . I went that night to
the house of a friend; and in the morning I sent
word to my parents and brother; and they came
for me. . . .

"Once every year I go to the temple of Kompira in Sanuki: all who have been saved from
shipwreck go there to give thanks. And I often
go to the temple of Jizō-Sama of Ogawa. If
you will come with me there to-morrow, I will
show you that plank."

Otokichi's Daruma

I

THE young folks are delighted, because last night a heavy fall of snow made for us what the Japanese poets so prettily call "a silver world." . . . Really these poets have been guilty of no extravagance in their charming praises of winter. For in Japan winter is beautiful, — fantastically beautiful. It bestirs no melancholy imaginings about "the death of nature," — inasmuch as nature remains most visibly alive during even the Period of Greatest Cold. It does not afflict the æsthetic eye with the spectacle of "skeleton-woods," — for the woods largely consist of evergreens. And the snow, — heaping softly upon the needles of the pines, or forcing the bamboos to display their bending grace under its momentary weight, — never suggests to Far-Eastern poet the dismal fancy of a winding-sheet. Indeed the singular charm of Japanese winter is made by this snow, — lumping itself into grotes-

267

queries unimaginable above the constant verdure of woods and gardens.

This morning my two students, Aki and Niimi, have been amusing themselves and the children by making a Yuki-Daruma; and I have been amusing myself by watching them. The rules for making a Yuki-Daruma are ancient and simple. You first compose a huge snowball, — between three and four feet in diameter, if possible, — which is to represent the squatting body of Daruma. Then you make a smaller snowball, about two feet in diameter, to represent his head; and you put this smaller ball on top of the other, — packing snow around the under-parts of both, so as to fix them in place. Two round lumps of charcoal serve to make eyes for Daruma; and some irregular fragments of the same material will suffice to indicate his nose and mouth. Finally, you must scoop out a hollow in the great belly of him, to represent a navel, and stick a lighted candle inside. The warmth of the candle gradually enlarges the opening. . . .

But I forgot to explain the term Yuki-Daruma, or Snow-Daruma. "Daruma" is an abbreviation of the name Bodai-Daruma, — Japanese rendering of the Sanscrit "Bodhidharma." And who was Bodhidharma?

Bodhidharma, or Bodhitara, was the twenty-eighth patriarch of Buddhism, by succession from the great Kâsyapa. He went to China as a Buddhist missionary in the first year of the Ryō dynasty [520 A. D.]; and in China he founded the great Zen (*Dhyâna*) sect,— whose doctrine is called "The Doctrine of Thought transmitted by Thought": that is to say, transmitted without words, either written or spoken. Says Professor Bunyiu Nanjio, in his *History of the Twelve Buddhist Sects* :— "Besides all the doctrines of the Mahâyâna and Hînayâna, there is one distinct line of transmission of a secret doctrine, which is not subject to any utterance at all. According to this doctrine, one is to see the so-called key to the thought of Buddha, or the nature of Buddha, directly by his own thought." The tradition of the Zen doctrine is curious. When the Buddha was preaching upon the Vulture Peak, there suddenly appeared before him the great Brahma, who presented a gold-colored flower to the Blessed One, and therewith besought him to preach the Law. The Blessed One accepted the heavenly

flower, and held it in his hand, but spoke no word.
Then the great assembly wondered at the silence
of the Blessed One.   But the venerable Kâsyapa
smiled.   And the Blessed One said to the venerable
Kâsyapa : — " I have the wonderful thought of
Nirvâna, the Eye of the True Law, which I now
shall give you." . . . So by thought alone the
doctrine was transmitted to Kâsyapa ; and by
thought alone Kâsyapa transmitted it to Ananda ;
and thereafter by thought alone it was transmitted
from patriarch to patriarch even to the time of
Bodhidharma, who communicated it to his successor, the second Chinese patriarch of the sect.
By some writers it is said that Bodhidharma
visited Japan ; but this statement appears to have
little foundation.   At all events, the Zen doctrine
was not introduced into Japan before the eighth
century.

Now of the many legends about Daruma, the
most famous is the story that he once remained
for nine years in uninterrupted meditation, during
which time his legs fell off.   Wherefore images
of him are made without legs.

Certainly Daruma has large claims to respect.
But the artists and the toymakers of the Far East
have never allowed these claims to interfere with

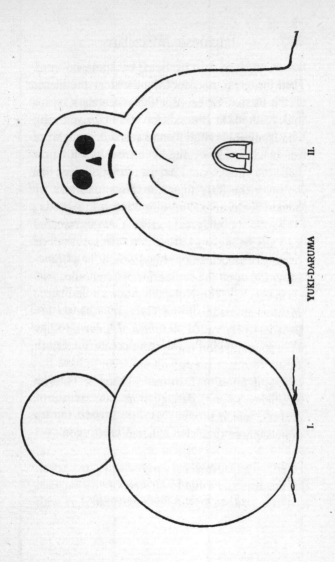

YUKI-DARUMA

the indulgence of their sense of humor, — originally bestirred, no doubt, by the story of the loss of his legs. For centuries this legendary mishap has been made the subject of comical drawings and comical carvings; and generations of Japanese children have amused themselves with a certain toy-image of Daruma so contrived that, however the little figure be thrown down, it will always bob up again into a squatting posture. This still popular toy, called *Okiagari-koboshi* ("The Getting-up Little Priest") may have been originally modelled, or remodelled, after a Chinese toy made upon the same principle, and called *Puh-Tau-Ung* ("The Not-falling-down Old Man"). Mention is made of the *Okiagari-Koboshi* in a Japanese play called *Manjū-Kui*, known to have been composed in the fourteenth century. But the earlier forms of the toy do not seem to have been representations of Daruma. There is, however, a children's-song, dating from the seventeenth century, which proves that the Daruma-toy was popular more than two hundred years ago: —

> *Hi ni! fu ni!*
> *Fundan Daruma ga*
> *Akai zukin kaburi sunmaita!*

["Once! twice! . . . Ever the red-hooded Daruma heedlessly sits up again!"]   From this little song it would seem that the form of the toy has not been much changed since the seventeenth century; Daruma still wears his hood, and is still painted red — all of him except his face.

Besides the Snow-Daruma already described, and the toy-Daruma (usually made of papier-mâché), there are countless comical varieties of Daruma: figures moulded or carved in almost every kind of material, and ranging in size from the tiny metal Daruma, half-an-inch long, designed for a pouch-clasp, to the big wooden Daruma, two or three feet high, which the Japanese tobacconist has adopted for a shop-sign. . . . Thus profanely does popular art deride the holy legend of the nine years' meditation.

TOY-DARUMA

II

Now that Yuki-Daruma in my garden reminds me of a very peculiar Daruma which I discovered several years ago, at a certain fishing-village on the eastern coast where I passed a happy

summer.   There was no hotel in the place; but a good man called Otokichi, who kept a fish-shop, used to let me occupy the upper part of his house, and fed me with fish cooked in a wonder-ful variety of ways.

One morning he called me into his shop to show me a very fine *hōbō*. . . . I wonder if you ever saw anything resembling a hōbō.   It looks so much like a gigantic butterfly or moth, that you must examine it closely to make sure that it is not an insect, but a fish, — a sort of gurnard. It has four fins arranged like pairs of wings, — the upper pair dark, with bright spots of sky-blue; the lower pair deep red. It seems also to have legs like a butterfly, — slender legs upon which it runs about quickly. . . .

"Is it good to eat?" I asked.

"*Hé!*" answered Otokichi: — "this shall be prepared for the Honorable Dinner."

[To any question asked of him, — even a question requiring answer in the negative, — Otokichi would begin his reply with the exclamation *Hé* ("Yes"), — uttered in such a tone of sympathy and good-will as to make the hearer immediately forget all the tribulations of existence.]

Then I wandered back into the shop, looking at things. On one side were rows of shelves supporting boxes of dried fish, and packages of edible seaweed, and bundles of straw sandals, and gourds for holding saké, and bottles of lemonade! On the opposite side, high up, I perceived the *kamidana*, — the Shelf of the Gods; and I noticed, under the *kamidana*, a smaller shelf occupied by a red image of Daruma. Evidently the image was not a toy: there were offerings in front of it. I was not surprised to find Daruma accepted as a household divinity, —because I knew that in many parts of Japan

prayers were addressed to him on behalf of children attacked by smallpox. But I was rather startled by the peculiar aspect of Otokichi's Daruma, which had only one eye, —a large and formidable eye that seemed to glare through the dusk of the shop like the eye of a great owl. It was the right eye, and was made of glazed paper. The socket of the left eye was a white void.

Therefore I called to Otokichi: —

"Otokichi San!— did the children knock out the left eye of Daruma Sama?"

"*Hé, hé!*" sympathetically chuckled Otokichi, — lifting a superb *katsuo* to the cutting-bench, — "he never had a left eye."

"Was he made that way?" I asked.

"*Hé!*" responded Otokichi, — as he swept his long knife soundlessly through the argent body, — "the folk here make only blind Darumas. When I got that Daruma, he had no eyes at all. I made the right eye for him last year, — after a day of great fishing."

"But why not have given him both eyes?" I queried; — "he looks so unhappy with only one eye!"

"*Hé, hé!*" replied Otokichi, — skilfully ranging the slices of pink-and-silver flesh upon a little mat of glass rods,[1] — "when we have another day of great good fortune, then he shall be given the other eye."

Then I walked about the streets of the village, peeping into the houses and shops; and I discovered various other Darumas in different stages

---

[1] Such a little glass mat is called *sudaré*.

of development, — some without eyes, some with
only one, and some with two. I remembered
that in Izumo it was especially Hotei, — the big-
bellied God of Comfort, — who used to be prac-
tically rewarded for his favors. As soon as the
worshipper found reason for gratitude, Hotei's
recumbent image was put upon a soft cushion;
and for each additional grace bestowed the god
would be given an additional cushion. But it
occurred to me that Daruma could not be given
more than two eyes: three would change him into
the sort of goblin called *Mitsumé-Kozō*. . . . I
learned, upon inquiry, that when a Daruma has
been presented with a pair of eyes, and with sundry small offerings, he is put away to make room
for an eyeless successor. The blind Daruma can
be expected to do wonderful things, because he
has to work for his eyes.

There are many such funny little deities in
Japan, — so many that it would need a very
big book to describe them; and I have found
that the people who worship these queer little
gods are, for the most part, pathetically honest.
Indeed my own experience would almost justify
the belief that the more artless the god, the

more honest the man, — though I do not want my reader to make any hasty deductions. I do not wish to imply, for example, that the superlative point of honesty might begin at the vanishing point of the god. Only this much I would venture : — Faith in very small gods, — toy-gods, — belongs to that simplicity of heart which, in this wicked world, makes the nearest possible approach to pure goodness.

On the evening before I left the village, Otokichi brought me his bill, — representing the cost of two months' good cheer;   and the amount proved to be unreasonably small. Of course a present was expected, according to the kindly Japanese custom; but, even taking that fact into consideration, the bill was absurdly honest. The least that I could do to show my appreciation of many things was to double the payment requested; and Otokichi's satisfaction, because perfectly natural and at the same time properly dignified, was something beautiful to see.

I was up and dressed by half-past three the next morning, in order to take an early express-train; but even at that ghostly hour I found

a warm breakfast awaiting me downstairs, and
Otokichi's little brown daughter ready to serve
me. . . . As I swallowed the final bowl of warm
tea, my gaze involuntarily wandered in the
direction of the household gods, whose tiny
lamps were still glowing. Then I noticed that
a light was burning also in front of Daruma;
and almost in the same instant I perceived that
Daruma was looking straight at me — WITH
TWO EYES! . . .

In a Japanese Hospital

I

. . . THE last patient of the evening, — a boy less than four years old, — is received by nurses and surgeons with smiles and gentle flatteries, to which he does not at all respond. . . . He is both afraid and angry — especially angry — at finding himself in an hospital to-night: some indiscreet person assured him that he was being taken to the theatre; — and he sang for joy on the way, forgetting the pain of his arm; — and this is not the theatre! There are doctors here — doctors that hurt people. . . . He lets himself be stripped, and bears the examination without wincing; but when told that he must lie down upon a certain low table, under an electric lamp, he utters a very emphatic *Iya !* [1] . . . The experience inherited from his ancestors has assured

---

[1] "No!"

him that to lie down in the presence of a possible
enemy is not good ; and by the same ghostly
wisdom he has divined that the smile of the sur-
geon was intended to deceive. . . . " But it will
be so nice upon the table ! " — coaxingly observes
a young nurse ; — " see the pretty red cloth ! "
" *Iya !* " repeats the little man — made only more
wary by this appeal to æsthetic sentiment. . . .
So they lay hands upon him — two surgeons and
two nurses, — lift him deftly, — bear him to the
table with the red cloth. Then he shouts his
small cry of war, — for he comes of good fighting stock, — and, to the general alarm, battles
most valiantly, in spite of that broken arm. But
lo ! a white wet cloth descends upon his eyes
and mouth, — and he cannot cry, — and there is
a strange sweet smell in his nostrils, — and the
voices and the lights have floated very, very far
away, — and he is sinking, sinking, sinking into
wavy darkness. . . . The slight limbs relax ; —
for a moment the breast heaves quickly, in the
last fight of the lungs against the paralyzing
anæsthetic : then all motion stops. . . . Now the
cloth is removed ; and the face reappears — all
the anger and pain gone out of it. So smile the
little gods that watch the sleep of the dead. . . .

Quickly the ends of the fractured bone are brought into place with a clear snap; — bandages and cotton and plaster-of-Paris, and yet more bandages, are rapidly applied by expert hands; — the face and little hands are sponged. Then the patient, still insensible, is wrapped in a blanket and taken away. . . . Interval, between entrance and exit : twelve minutes and a half.

Nothing is commonplace as seen for the first time; and the really painless details of the incident — the stifling of the cry, the sudden numbing of will, the subsequent pallid calm of the little face — so simulated tragedy as to set imagination wandering in darksome ways. . . . A single wicked blow would have produced exactly the same results of silence and smiling rest. Countless times in the countless ages of the past it must have done so ; — countless times passion must have discerned, in the sudden passionless beauty of the stricken, the eternal consequence of the act. . . . *Till the heavens be no more they shall not awake, nor be roused out of their sleep.* " Till the heavens be no more " — but after ? Thereafter — perhaps : yet never again the same. . . .

But I felt that I had been startled more than touched by that sudden suppression of the personality, the Self, — because of the mystery thereby made manifest. In one moment, — under the vapor of a chemical, — voice, motion, will, thought, all pleasure and pain and memory, had ceased to be; — the whole life of the budding senses, — the delicate machinery of the little brain, with its possible priceless inheritance from countless generations, — had been stilled and stopped as by the very touch of death. And there remained, to all outward seeming, only the form, the simulacrum, — a doll of plastic flesh, with the faint unconscious smile of an icon. . . .

The faces of the little stone Buddhas, who dream by roadsides or above the graves, have the soft charm of Japanese infancy. They resemble the faces of children asleep; — and you must have seen Japanese children asleep to know the curious beauty of the immature features, — the vague sweetness of the lines of lids and lips. In the art of the Buddhist image-maker, the peace of the divine condition is suggested by the same shadowy smile that makes beautiful the slumber of the child.

II

THE memory of icons naturally evoked remembrance of those powers which icons do but symbolize ; and presently I found myself thinking that, to the vision of a God, the entire course of a human life would appear much like the incident which I had just witnessed, — a coming, a crying and struggling, and a sudden vanishing of personality under the resistless anæsthetic of death. (I am not speaking of a cosmic divinity, to whom the interval between the kindling and the extinction of a sun would seem as brief as seems to us the flash of a firefly in the night: I mean an anthropomorphic God.) According to Herbert Spencer, the tiny consciousness of a gnat can distinguish intervals of time representing something between the ten-thousandth and the fifteen-thousandth part of a second. For a being as mentally superior to man as man to the gnat, would not the time of a generation appear but an instant ? Would such a being perceive our human existence at all, except as a budding and a withering, — a ceaseless swift succession of apparitions and disparitions, — a mere phenomenon of fermentation peculiar to the surface of a cooling planet? Of course, were he to study that phenomenon in detail, somewhat as we study ferments under the lens, he would not see the smile of the babe change instantaneously to the laughter of the skull ; — but I fancy that whatever might psychologically happen, between the first smile of rosy flesh and the last dull grin of bone, would remain for him as indistinguishable as the gnat's ten or fifteen thousand wing-beats per second remain for us. I doubt whether the God of a system, or even of a single world, could sympathize with our emotions any more than we ourselves can sympathize with the life that thrills in a droplet of putrid water. . . .

But what is this human creature that, in the sight of a God, might seem to rise from earth merely to weep and laugh one moment in the light, ere crumbling back to clay again? A form evolved, in the course of a hundred million years, from out some shapeless speck of primordial slime. But this knowledge of the evolution nowise illuminates the secret of the life in itself, — the secret of the sentiency struggling against destruction through all those million centuries, — ever contriving and building, to baffle death, more and more astounding complexities of substance, more and yet more marvellous complexities of mind, — and able at last to prolong the term of its being from the primal duration of an instant to the possible human age of a hundred years. The sentiency is the riddle of riddles. Thought has been proved a compounding of sensation. But the simplest sensation perceptible is itself a compound or the result of a compounding, — perhaps the shock of a fusion, — the flash of a blending; — and the mystery of life remains the most inscrutable, the most tremendous, the most appalling of enigmas.

From the terror of that mystery our fathers sought to save their world by uttering the black decree: — " *On pain of sword and fire, — on peril of the Everlasting Death,* — THOU SHALT NOT THINK! "

But the elder wisdom of the East proclaimed: " *Fear not to think, O child of the Abyss, upon the Depth that gave thee birth! Divining that Formless out of which thou hast come, into which thou must dissolve again, thou shalt know thy Being timeless, and infinitely One! . . .*"